GCSE Graphic Products for OCR

Geoff Hancock

RECOGNISING ACHIEVEMENT

Heinemann Educational
Halley Court, Jordan Hill, Oxford OX2 8 EJ
Part of Harcourt Education

Heinemann is the registered trademark of
Harcourt Education Limited

First published in 2001

10 09 08 07 06
10 9 8 7 6 5 4

British Library Cataloguing in Publication Data
A catalogue record for this book is available from the
British Library

10-digit ISBN: 0 435 41740 1
13-digit ISBN: 978 0 435417 40 6

Typeset by Artistix, Thame, Oxon
Printed and bound in Spain by Mateu Cromo.

Acknowledgements

The author would like to thank all the students who
throughout his career have, through their efforts and
endeavours, made teaching so rewarding. The author
would particularly like to thank those whose work has
contributed to this book: Judith Brownbill, Peter Simmons,
Jasmine Armour-Marshall, Lauren Dicker and many others
from the Kings of Wessex Community School in Cheddar.

The publishers would like to thank the following for
permission to reproduce photographs:
Apple (iMac) on p.7; Art Directors/Trip pp.126 (bottom),
127 (left), 268, 269; Gareth Boden pp.8 (top), 20 (both),
21 (top), 31 (left), 36, 49, 92 (left), 94, 98 (top left and
right, bottom left), 147 (top left and bottom left); Giles
Chapman Library pp.7 (new mini), 64, 93, 98 (all), 98
(bottom right); 109 (top), 128 (bottom), 129, 146 (top left
and bottom left), Corbis pp.7 (fashion models), 56, 62,
121, 124 (left), 137 (right); Trevor Clifford pp.7 (film
poster), 9 (both), 11, 21 (bottom), 30, 41, 44, 47, 48, 53,
60, 61, 68 (tube map, display), 84, 86 (both), 87 (both);
88 (both), 89, 92, 95, 100, 103, 106, 107, 107, 109
(bottom), 110 (election and film posters), 120 (montage),
124 (right), 126 (top), 128 (top), 137 (left), 148; Empics
pp.69 (top), 99, 111 (bottom); Epson pp.125 (both), 135,
138 (bottom right); Chris Honeywell p.96 (bottom left);
Chris Honeywell/Collections p.123; Peter Morris pp.10
(right), 68 (danger sign, magazine cover, car plate, car
badge, Canadian bus graphic), 76, 96 (top), 102, 108, 110
(Keble poster), 111 (toys courtesy of Kit Morris), 112, 116
(left), 132, 133 (bottom), 138 (left), 139, 154 (student
portfolio); Morgana p.133 (top); Photodisc pp.69, 121,
136; Photo objects pp.97 (telephones), 140; Martin
Sookias p.103 (right); Techsoft p.147; V & A Museum
p.120 (bottom right picture of 'The Courtesan Itsutomi
with a Samisen' by Hosoda Eishi).

The publishers would like to thank the following for
permission to use copyright material:
AA (The Automobile Association Ltd) for the logo on
p.106; Benetton and Modus Publicity for the Benetton
advertisements on pp.101, 104; Bollé/Serengetti for the
Bollé advertisement on p.104; Cadbury for the website
image on p.15, the logo on p.107, the creme egg on p.88,
the point of sale display on p.20, the chocolate bars on p21;
Chicken for the eggs on p.88; Dr. Martens for all the images
on pp.42–3 and the poster on p.112; The Estée Lauder
companies for the use of the Origins logo; Kellogs for use
of logos on p.106, McDonald's Restaurants Ltd for use of
the logo on pp.107, 109; Morgana Systems Ltd; adapted
questions on pp.46, 82, 100, 134 and 148 reproduced
with the kind permission of OCR; the 'Missing – an
education' poster and logos on pp.104, 106 reproduced
with permission of Oxfam Publishing, 274 Banbury Road,
Oxford, OX2 7DZ; Nestlé for the chocolate bars on p.113
and 118; Lisa Robinson for her excellent support; SfE for
the website image on p.143 and other images with the SfE
logo on p.107; © All rights reserved, Shell International
Oil Company Limited for the logo on p.106; Swatch
Group UK for the logos on p.113; the working drawing on
p.145 courtesy of Techsoft UK Ltd; Walkers Snack Foods
Ltd for the logo and crisp packets on pp.44–5.

The publishers have made every effort to contact
copyright holders. However, if any material has been
incorrectly acknowledged, the publishers would be
pleased to correct this at the earliest opportunity

Contents

Introduction

This book has been written to meet the specification requirements for the OCR GCSE in Design and Technology: Graphic Products. The book covers all the requirements for the short and full courses. Extra material and exemplification is contained within the Teacher's Resource File.

The OCR specification content provides a range of opportunities to develop design and technology capability through activities, including:

- product **analysis** and **evaluation**
- focused tasks
- extended task where you will design and make quality graphic products.

You will be assessed in two ways. You will have to do a coursework project which is worth 60% of the GCSE and must take you no more than 40 hours to complete (20 hours for the short course). In addition, you will sit two examination papers, each worth 20% of the GCSE.

How to use the book

The book is divided into the following sections:

- Design in Action
- Communicating Design
- Realizing Design
- Get the Message?
- The Final Print
- Using ICT
- Internal Assessment.

The book is written in a series of double-page spreads. Each double-page spread includes:

- specification links – these show which sections of the specification are covered by the double-page spread
- questions – these test knowledge and understanding and can be used in independent study and for revision
- key points – these give you a summary of some of the most important points covered on the double-page spread.

Symbols are used on the spreads to show work covering ICT and industrial practice:

  indicates ICT

  indicates industrial practice.

At the end of each section there is a set of more detailed questions that test your knowledge and understanding of the specification content covered. These can be used for home study and revision.

The book is supported by a Teacher's Resource File (TRF), which provides more information on certain topics, proformas for coursework, and activities to help develop your design and technology skills.

  indicates supplementary work in TRF.

This book covers all the extra knowledge, skills and understanding needed to achieve the highest grade at GCSE. The book does not include information about materials and tools that are used within the Key Stage 3 curriculum. Tools such as coping saws and junior hacksaws should be well known to you and are therefore not repeated within this book.

Notes for teachers

The aims of the OCR GCSE in Design and Technology: Graphic Products specification are:

- to encourage candidates to combine their designing and making skills with knowledge and understanding, in order to design and make quality products

- to promote design and technology capability in candidates through activities which involve a range of contexts, materials and processes and lead to practical outcomes

- to give opportunities to develop practical abilities and confidence to design, make and modify products for intended purposes, selecting and using resources effectively

- to promote the use of graphic techniques and ICT, including computer-aided design (CAD), to generate, develop, model and communicate design proposals

- to promote the use of computer-aided manufacture (CAM) in single-item production and in batch or volume production

- to encourage the development of candidates' critical and aesthetic abilities, enabling them to evaluate design and technology activity, including their own, in the context of an identified need

- to encourage the development of candidates' understanding of the needs and values of a range of users, including spiritual, moral, social and cultural considerations

- to promote the key skills of communication, application of number, ICT, working with others, improving learning and performance and problem solving

- to encourage the development of candidates' thinking skills, financial capability, enterprise and entrepreneurial skills

- to encourage the development of candidates' understanding of work-related learning and the principles of sustainable design and production systems

- to encourage candidates to consider how present and past design and technology, relevant to a designing and making process, affects society

- to encourage candidates to consider issues and effects of new technologies and modern materials on product design and manufacture

- to provide for activities which give candidates opportunities to work both individually and in teams.

Examination

The terminal examination papers will test candidates' knowledge and understanding of Graphic Products through questions on designing and making.

Further information

Whilst this book provides a comprehensive coverage of the main content for the OCR Graphic Products specification, additional resources may be useful. In particular, the *Skills in Graphic Products* pupil book (Heinemann) provides alternative questions and ideas. The *Skills in Graphic Products Teachers' Resource Pack* (Heinemann) provides a wide range of templates, activities and information that will directly support the teaching of the specification. Further information can be found on the Internet. A list of useful web site addresses can be found in the Teacher's Resource File.

DESIGN IN ACTION

Graphic products at large

We use a wide range of graphic products in our everyday lives

Graphics are everywhere

It is hard to imagine any aspect of our lives that is not influenced or affected by graphic products. From what we wear to what we eat, **designers** are using graphic products to persuade, sell and communicate things. Graphic products are things that use pictures or words to sell, protect or communicate either themselves or other products. You are currently reading a graphic product. All books communicate information. They use text and graphics in the form of pictures and diagrams. They often have a hard cover to protect the inside pages and they have interesting graphics on the front cover to help sell them.

Graphic products are nearly always made from paper, card or plastic. They can be two dimensional (2D) or three dimensional (3D).

2D products

A good example of a 2D graphic product is a postage stamp. Made from thin paper, stamps communicate information and use interesting graphic images to help sell them and grab attention. Although stamps have one basic **function** (to pay for the costs of postage) their designs are constantly being changed. There are two types of stamps – plain, simple stamps and very decorative ones.

Stamps – 2D graphic products

3D products

A good example of a 3D product is washing powder packaging. Cardboard is used for dry powder and plastic for liquid. The packages use colour graphics to make them interesting and attractive and bold text that stands out. Think about the different colours they use as well. Why are white and blue often used on products that are used for cleaning rather than brown or grey?

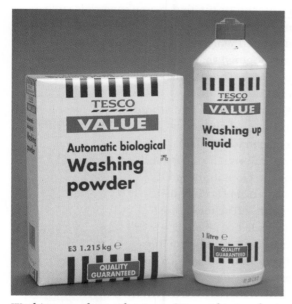

Washing powder packaging – 3D graphic products

Elements of a graphic product

The main elements of a graphic product are the text, the pictures or images and the style or layout.

The digital video disc (DVD) is a common household product that shows these three elements well.

The example of the DVD shows that, within a graphic product, there is often a range of components or parts. These are all graphic products themselves. In the photo to the right, there is the case which protects the DVD, the inlay which communicates information about it and creates interest, and the surface printing on the DVD itself which also communicates information and interests anyone seeing it.

A DVD and its case show the main elements of a graphic product

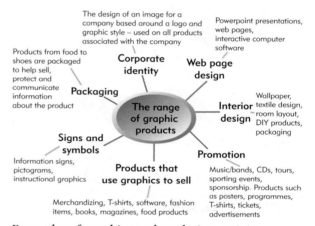

The design of an image for a company based around a logo and graphic style – used on all products associated with the company

Powerpoint presentations, web pages, interactive computer software

Products from food to shoes are packaged to help sell, protect and communicate information about the product

Corporate identity

Web page design

Packaging

The range of graphic products

Interior design — Wallpaper, textile design, room layout, DIY products, packaging

Signs and symbols

Information signs, pictograms, instructional graphics

Promotion

Music/bands, CDs, tours, sporting events, sponsorship. Products such as posters, programmes, T-shirts, tickets, advertisements

Products that use graphics to sell

Merchandizing, T-shirts, software, fashion items, books, magazines, food products

Examples of graphic product design activity

Activities

1 Which type of stamp do you think is the most popular – a plain, simple stamp or a decorative one like that on the opposite page? Why?

2 Why are white and blue often used on cleaning products? Give reasons.

Key points

● Graphic products use pictures or words to sell, protect or communicate.

● Graphic products can be 2D or 3D.

● The main elements of a graphic product are the text, image and layout.

Safety and the environment

Working safely

What unsafe working practices can you spot?

When **designing** and making graphic products, both in industry and at school, personal safety is always the most important consideration. Everyone who operates machinery or uses equipment that is potentially hazardous is responsible in law for the safety of themselves and others. Industrial employers and schools must ensure that individuals are trained about safety and that all necessary equipment is available to use.

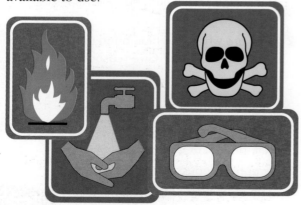

Safety signs found in the working environment

Hazardous materials

Materials, such as adhesives, often contain toxic elements, such as solvents, which can be harmful if touched or inhaled. Some materials such as manufactured boards create fine dust when machined which is carcinogenic (contains carcinogens) that can lead to cancer. These substances must be carefully controlled, used and stored and their usage must conform to COSHH regulations. COSHH stands for the Containment Of Substances Hazardous to Health. All schools must have a list of all such substances with guidelines about their safe storage and use.

All materials used within design and technology that are potentially hazardous to individuals must be clearly labelled and safe procedures for their use must be provided.

Solvent-based glues must display a hazard warning

Assessing the risk

Whenever you carry out a making procedure, you should assess the potential risks involved to you and identify safe procedures to avoid or minimize the risk to your health and safety. This is called risk assessment and is a three-part process:

1 Write a production plan of the whole manufacturing process.

2 Make a list of all the potential hazards you will face when using the machinery or equipment.

3 Write procedures that will ensure you minimize the risks.

Protecting the environment

Victor Papenek once said that we are living in a 'Kleenex Culture'. By this he meant that people do not buy things to keep anymore. Cars are kept for three years and changed, people move house regularly, products, such as razors, cups and plates are disposable, made to be thrown away. Every time a product is made, used and discarded, enormous amounts of energy are wasted. It takes more energy to produce a dry-cell battery than there is energy in it. As design and technologists we have a responsibility to consider the environmental effects of our design decisions.

It takes more energy to produce a battery than there is energy in it. The alternative is to use a rechargeable battery that can be recharged up to a thousand times

Recycling

Materials that were once simply discarded such as paper, card, plastics and steel are now being recycled. Recycling is very often cost effective as well as environmentally friendly. The advantages of recyling are clear:

- It conserves valuable non-renewable resources, such as oil, coal and gas.
- It reduces energy consumption.
- It helps to reduce emissions and pollution.

Pollution

We have all heard about global warming and its effect upon the climate. But many other forms of pollution occur that are hazardous to the environment. Untreated chemicals, such as oil that leak into rivers and streams, can have an adverse effect upon ecosystems and the natural balance in different environments. The discarding of glass and other dangerous equipment is both hazardous to people and animals and can easily be avoided.

As design and technologists it is important that the environmental and social consequences of our designing and making activities are fully taken into consideration at all stages of the process. One way that designers and manufacturers can assess the impact of their product is to carry out a life cycle analysis (LCA). Life cycle analysis involves accurately measuring the lifetime of a product from the initial extraction of raw materials through to its final disposal. By carrying out LCA, manufacturers can then develop ways of extending the life of a product and so reduce its negative effect on the environment.

Activities

1 Explain what is meant by the term risk assessment.

2 Give three advantages of recycling.

3 Explain what is meant by the term life cycle analysis.

Key points

- We are all responsible for our own safety and the safety of others. Legal requirements, such as COSHH rules, are designed to ensure a safe working environment.
- Recycling helps to reduce energy use and pollution and conserves the earth's natural resources.
- Life cycle analysis is a process that is used to develop ways of extending the life of products and so make them more environmentally friendly.

The design process

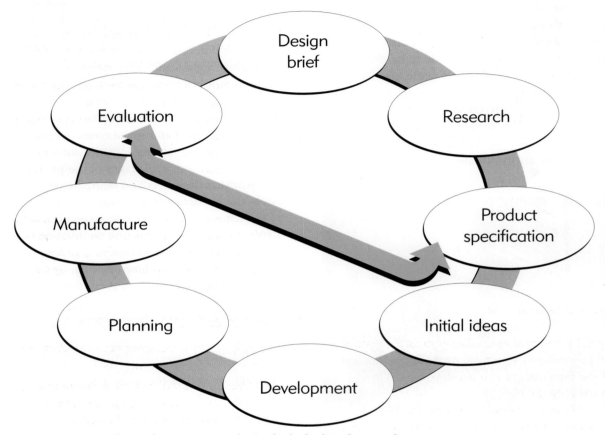

The design process – the evaluation must always be linked to the specification

A common link

The **design** process is the common link that binds all design and technology subjects together. Designing is about using a wide range of skills and knowledge to make quality products. Projects may range from the design of advertizing leaflets and promotional materials through to challenging projects, such as film sets and web pages.

Look carefully at the design process above and you will see that it goes in a circle. You can start anywhere on that circle, although usually you start with a **brief** and finish with the **evaluation**.

The brief

Usually graphic designers are given a **brief** by a client. A brief is a short, clear statement which says what is needed. Imagine you were asked to design a new promotional display for a range of jeans using the catchphrase 'Don't look back in Wranglers'. The brief might simply say: 'Design and make a **point of sale** display for Wranglers jeans using the title "Don't look back in Wranglers"'.

Sometimes graphic designers will have to write a brief themselves. This usually happens when they have their own ideas which they will later try and sell to a client.

Analysing the brief

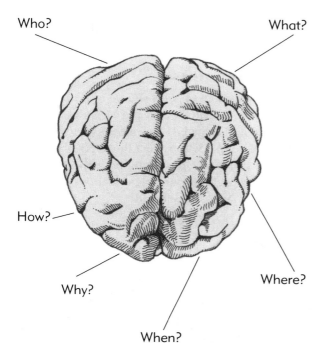

Who?

What?

How?

Why?

Where?

When?

How to analyse a brief

A brief is a very simple statement and does not tell you enough about the problem. To find out all the information you need, you have to **analyse** the brief.

Analysing the brief simply means asking questions to find out what you can and cannot do. A good starting point for this is to use the 5WH approach to analysis. 5WH stands for 'Who?, What?, Where?, When?, Why? (and How?)'. Here are some of the questions you might ask for a jeans point of sale display:

Who?   Who are the range of users (the **target market**)? Which age group is the product aimed at? What is their sex? What images would you associate with them?

What?   What has the product got to do (its **function/s**)? What size, shape does it need to be? Are certain materials to be used? What images, titles and colours need to be used?

Where?   Where will it be displayed? Will this affect its design, weight, properties? Can it go outside? Is it waterproof?

When?   When must it be finished (what is the deadline)? When is the promotion due to start?

Why?   Why is it needed? Is there an alternative? Why must it be a particular shape, size, colour, material?

How?   How will it be made? How much will it cost? How will the cost affect the decisions I need to make? How will I plan my time to make sure all the deadlines are met? What is the quantity needed and how will this affect my chosen method of production?

Some of the answers to these questions will be easy and some will be difficult. In order to be sure that you have all the correct answers to enable you to design the product you must now carry out **research**.

Activities

1   Explain why a designer could start at any point on the design process.

2   Think carefully about the following three products and write a design brief that might have been given for each:

   a   stationery for a new restaurant

   b   packaging for sports shoes

   c   a fizzy drink called Yabba dabba do.

3   Chose a CD from a band of your choice and carry out a 5WH analysis. What would be the main points you would need to include in a design brief for this CD?

Key points

● A design brief is a simple, clear statement about the problem or need.

● The analysis should come after the design brief and not be part of it.

Doing research

Research means the process of finding out information, **analysing** the information and then drawing conclusions about it that will help your designing. Research is not something that is done at the beginning of a project and forgotten about. It should be carried out at many stages during the entire process as new problems arise. Every time you ask someone a question, browse the Internet or look in a book, you are carrying out research.

It is very easy to fill up your project with pages and pages of printouts from the Internet. Research will be of little value unless it is relevant and **analysed**.

There are two main types of research:

● primary

● secondary.

Primary research

Primary research is often called first-hand research. It includes activities such as visits and interviews and is a very good way of researching a problem because you can find out for yourself what the problems are and see things in real life, rather than having a second-hand view of it. Primary sources include:

● visits and interviews

● conducting **surveys** or consumer trials

● carrying out product analysis of existing products

● **questionnaires**

● taking photographs.

One of the most effective methods of research is to conduct a user survey. Users are people who either use the product you are intending to design or are within the target age group. You can use questionnaires in a user survey.

Questionnaires

Questionnaires are a good source of primary information, providing they are carefully **designed** and targeted. This means choosing a sample of people who reflect the users of the intended product. Questionnaires are particularly useful for finding out about user preference, such as preferred:

● colour

● shape

● cost

● materials.

Great care needs to be taken when writing a questionnaire to ensure the questions are understood and not misinterpreted.

When writing a questionnaire, follow these rules:

● Avoid questions that require long answers.

● Ask questions that are quick to answer.

● Only ask questions that will give you useful information.

● Use tick boxes where possible.

Analysing questionnaires

The information collected from questionnaires will have no value unless it is analysed so that you can draw conclusions from it about your own design brief. Use these questions to analyse your results:

● What key things do the users prefer?

● What proof do I have?

● How will the results of the questionnaire influence my design **specification**?

● Does the questionnaire help me to make decisions about such things as colour, shape, cost, materials, weight, **function**?

Using a database

A computer **database** is a good tool to use to help you analyse the results of your questionnaires. Databases are designed to store and retrieve a vast amount of information. You would set up a record for each person who answered the questionnaire. Each individual question is called a field.

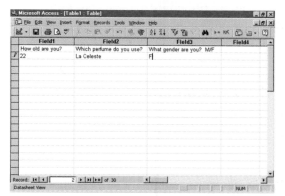

A *database screen showing the results from a questionnaire*

Once the information has been stored on the database it is easy to use. The database will allow you to sort (put into a particular order) and search the information. For example, it could give you a list of answers in alphabetical or age order. More complex searches allow you to ask more than one question at a time. For example, how many fifteen-year-olds who eat crisps prefer cheese and onion? Using a database is also a good way of using ICT in your coursework.

Secondary research

Secondary research is easier to carry out than primary research. It involves looking through work produced by other people. Books, compact discs (CDs) and the Internet are a rich and valuable source of secondary information. Secondary sources include:

- books
- magazines
- CD-ROM
- the Internet
- experts.

The Internet is a very useful source of information

As part of your GCSE, you must use ICT within your coursework. Carrying out research on the computer is a very good way of doing this. **Websites** on the Internet have pages and pages of information that will help you. You can also e-mail companies to ask for brochures and information about their products. See pages 136–47 for more about ICT.

Activities

1 Explain what is meant by the term **target market**.

2 Explain how a database can be a useful tool for design research.

Key points

- There are two types of research – primary and secondary.
- Questionnaires must be carefully planned if they are going to provide useful information.
- Questionnaires will be of little value unless the information gathered is recorded and analysed.
- The conclusions drawn should influence your design specification.

Information and data presentation

The outcomes of research

After you have carried out your **research**, you will often have a great deal of information. As part of the process of **analysis**, you should clearly present the findings in a graphical form, so that people can instantly see the results. A picture, graph or chart is much easier to understand and remember than a set of figures.

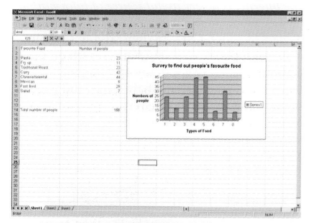

A comparison of written information and a chart

Types of information

There are basically two types of information that come from the results of research:

● information that can be measured

● information that cannot be measured.

Quantitative information

Information that can be measured is called **quantitative** information. This type of information is usually produced from **questionnaires** where everybody is asked exactly the same question. The results can be **analysed** and conclusions drawn.

Quantitative research allows you to make judgements such as: 75% of the people asked in the age range 14–18 years said that they prefer … whereas only 15% of those in the 35–45 age

range said … hence this product would be better suited to 14–18-year-olds. Quantitative information is exact and is quantifiable.

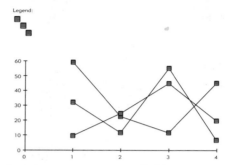

A graph giving quantitative information

Qualitative information

Information that cannot be measured is called **qualitative** information. This type of information is usually produced from observations and interviews and is useful for giving people's opinions or ideas. This type of information often shows trends or patterns of choice.

Example of a qualitative chart showing a trend

Presenting information

The presentation of results is an important stage in the design process. The type of graph or chart that is chosen not only helps to communicate the information, but also makes the information more interesting. The three main types of charts used are pie charts, line graphs and bar charts.

Pie charts

It is often useful to present the information you have gained from quantitative research as a percentage of the whole. This is particularly important when you need to use information in order to make a decision. Pie charts are a quick visual way of showing the preferences of the people asked, for example.

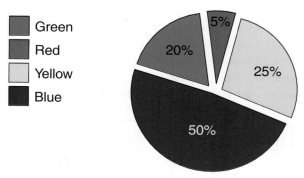

- Green
- Red
- Yellow
- Blue

5%
20%
25%
50%

A pie chart

Line graphs

The most common type of graph used for displaying quantitative information is the line graph. A line graph simply uses a line to connect a series of points or crosses on a graph. Line graphs are a useful way of showing trends over time.

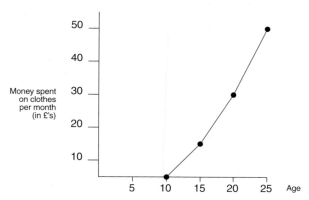

Money spent on clothes per month (in £'s)

A line graph

Bar charts

Sometimes it is useful to make a comparison of results. For example, one way of comparing the results of a questionnaire to find out your classmates' favourite colour is to draw a bar chart. A bar chart (often referred to as a histogram)

enables you quickly to make a visual comparison of the answers to questions. It is very easy with a bar chart to see the biggest and smallest in any category.

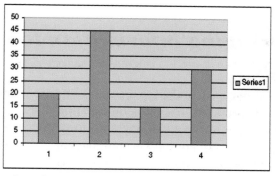

A bar chart

Line graphs, bar charts and pie charts are usually two-dimensional (2D). These charts can be made more interesting by using ICT to produce three-dimensional (3D) graphs and charts. Computers can help you to present charts quickly and easily.

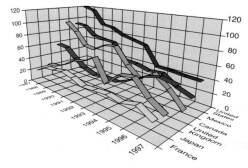

A line graph presented in 3D

Activity

1 Explain the advantage of using a chart to display information rather than a **database** or set of figures.

Key points

- There are two main types of data – quantitative and qualitative.
- Quantitative data can be measured and quantified. Qualitative data shows impressions and trends; it is not directly measurable.

Charts, graphs and displays

Bringing information to life

So far we have looked at the standard graphs and charts used for presenting information. Bar charts, pie charts and line graphs form the basis of most information presentations.

However, graphic **designers** often look for more exciting and interesting ways of presenting information. This is particularly important when a company is trying to produce information in order to promote its products.

Charts can have particular impact when they are used to communicate **qualitative** data. In the example below, the designer has chosen to use the representation of a wave to show how seaside holidays are on the increase. Another example of communicating qualitative data could be an apple core to show how the world's resources are being eaten away.

This type of chart does not show exact figures, but it shows a trend and has a strong impact as a graphic image.

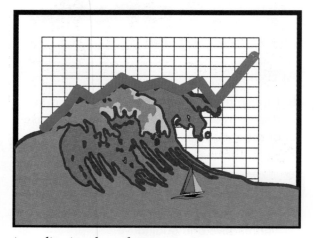

A qualitative chart that creates impact

Using pictograms

A **pictogram** is a graphic symbol that is used instead of words. It takes up less space and does not rely on people speaking the same language. Pictograms are often so well known that they are used all around the world as standardized symbols. Look carefully at the six pictograms below – what do they represent?

Well known pictograms

Pictograms in graphs and charts

When pictograms are used in graphs and charts in order to bring them to life, they are called pictographs. For example, the pictographs on the opposite page make the information more visually interesting and relevant.

Pictograms can be used to represent the bars in a bar chart. This helps to communicate the results and create interest.

As part of GCSE coursework within graphic products, pictographs can be used for representing the results of your research. They can add quality to your work and give you an opportunity to show both creativity and designing skills.

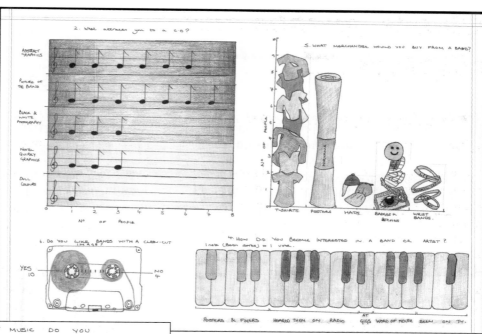

Student pictographs show how information can be made more visually interesting and relevant

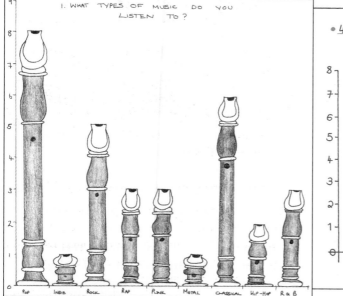

Activities

1 List four standard graphic symbols used on products such as CD players.

2 Explain the advantages of using pictograms in graphic products such as holiday brochures.

3 Design a pictograph for presenting the results of a questionnaire on people's favourite sports.

Key points

● Pictograms are symbols that communicate information without the use of words. They are simple, take up less space and cross language barriers.

● Graphs or charts that use graphic symbols are called pictographs

Product analysis 1

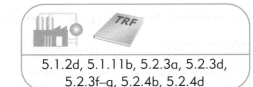

5.1.2d, 5.1.11b, 5.2.3a, 5.2.3d,
5.2.3f–g, 5.2.4b, 5.2.4d

Looking carefully at existing products that are similar to the one you are going to **design** is a very important part of the design process. To learn successfully from existing products you have to look at them with a 'critical eye'. Looking critically at products and asking questions about them is known as product **analysis**.

Analysing graphic products

When you analyse a product, you should always use the 5WH approach (see page 13). This will act as a good starting point.

For example, a **point of sale** display is a graphic product, so if you were analysing the point of sale display in the photo below, you might ask the following questions.

A point of sale display

Who is the product aimed at?

To answer this question, you have to think of the type of product being promoted. For example, soap powder is usually aimed at adults. Look to see if there are any visual clues. A visual clue is anything that helps you to understand what the designer's intentions were. It may be a picture, a style of writing or a particular choice of colours.

What is the purpose of the point of sale display?

The display has to hold leaflets, but how many? Does the number of leaflets it needs to hold affect its size? The leaflets are usually made to a standard size that could be A4, A5 or even A6. This is because paper is more easily available in these sizes.

Holding leaflets is probably the primary **function** (or main purpose) of the point of sale display. It will also have secondary functions of attracting attention to the product being **advertized** on the leaflets and helping to sell it.

What material has been used and why?

Cardboard is usually used for point of sale displays. There are several reasons for this:

● Cardboard is cheaper than **acrylic**. This is important because usually point of sale displays only have to last for as long as the product promotion.

● It is easy to print on to. This helps to keep costs down.

● It can be folded flat for delivery. This is important for transportation and storage.

Why is this point of sale leaflet holder made out of cardboard instead of acrylic?

Graphic products are often ephemeral, or short-lived

Items like tickets and posters are designed to last for a very short period of time and then they are thrown away. One of the most important questions for you to ask is 'How does the fact that many graphic products are ephemeral (short-lived) affect their design and manufacture?'.

A range of short-lived graphic products

Comparative analysis

Sometimes it is useful to compare graphic products to find out why the same product has been designed differently. A good example of this is sweets. There are hundreds of different types of sweets that are all more or less the same and have the same function – being eaten!

The same basic product – chocolate – has been designed differently. Why are there so many different varieties of the same basic product?

Comparing products helps you to answer the question 'Why?':

- *Why* are different colours used?
  Red is commonly used because it really stands out. Think of other colours and what they do.
- *Why* do products aimed at children look different to products designed for teenagers, or adults?
  This will help you to understand about different markets. A market is the type of people who use a certain product.
- *Why* do products have different types of packaging and use different materials?
  This will help you to understand about production and packaging techniques, and why some products have to be completely sealed.

Activities

1 Give two reasons why designers carry out product analysis as part of the design process.

2 Graphic products are nearly always short-lived or throw-away (such as packaging). Describe two ethical issues related to the growing use of graphic products to sell and promote other products

Key points

- Product analysis (sometimes called disassembly) is an important form of primary **research**.
- A useful framework for analysing products is the 5WH approach:
  - Who?
  - What?
  - Where?
  - When?
  - Why?
  - (and How?)
- Because graphic products are designed to be ephemeral (short-lived) they need to be low cost.

Product analysis 2

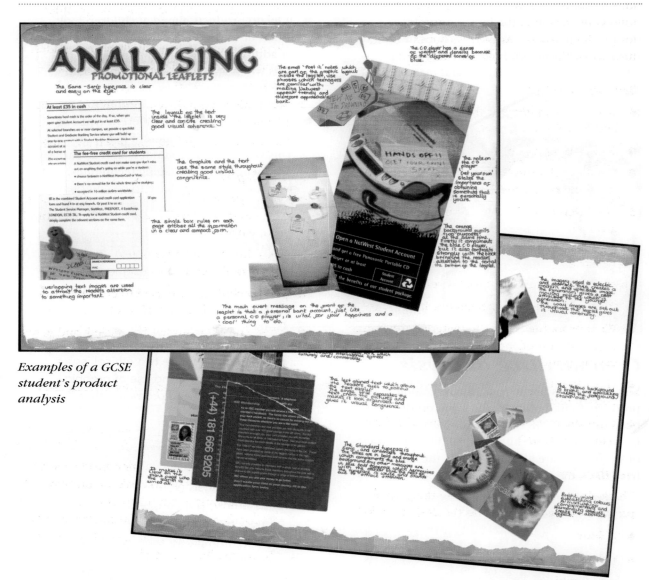

Examples of a GCSE student's product analysis

Look carefully at the two examples of product **analysis** taken from a student's GCSE coursework. The key features of successful product analysis are that the work should:

- be thoroughly analysed against a set of **criteria**

- answer questions that will lead to a **specification** for your own product

- be well presented.

Establish a list of main points or considerations to help with your own **research** and remember that product analysis does not merely describe a product. It always uses the 5WH approach (see page 13).

The best examples of product analysis should contain **evaluations** and conclusions.

A product analysis checklist

When carrying out product analysis it is a good idea to use a prompt sheet to help you. The following questions can be used as a framework for product analysis. Answer each question in turn about the product you are analysing.

Target market

- What is the market for the product or service, and how do you know?
- Who uses it/buys it?
- Are there clues in the text/colours/graphics to show the **target market**?
- Are different styles used for different age groups?

Materials

The correct choice of material is very important.

- What material(s) have been used, and why?
- What properties does the material used need? (e.g. waterproof, strong, stiff, lightweight, easy to print on to)
- How does the cost of the product affect the chosen material?
- Does the method of manufacture affect the chosen material?

Aesthetics

Think about the things that make the graphic product look good. How has the designer used:

- colour
- balance
- symmetry?

Ergonomics

- Is the product easy to use?
- How has the designer taken the user into account?
- Are there specific sizes taken into account? Is the style and size of type easy to read and clear?

Communication

Think about how the information contained on the graphic product is conveyed to the buyer:

- Is it overt – this means open or obvious? Is it easy to tell the message from the graphic?
- Is it covert – this means hidden? Sometimes the message or image is deliberately hidden to make people really think deeply about a product. If so, why?
- What information is required by law for this product?
- Does it use symbols or images? If so, why?

Typography

- What style of text is used? Is it serif, sans serif or stylised (see page 112)? Is there a mixture? If so, why?
- Does the size and style of text affect the impact of the graphic?
- What techniques are used to create impact? (e.g. size, colour, style of type)
- What type of layout has been used, and why? (e.g. left, right, centre justification – see page 113)
- What drawing systems/ICT have been used and why?

Activity

1 Look carefully at a common product such as a chocolate bar and ask the question 'What convinces people to buy this product/service rather than similar brands or alternatives?'. (Think about the design, the words, the messages.)

Key point

- Graphic products are successful when they attract, create interest, create desire and lead to action (people buying or using the product). Product analysis can help to discover how **designers** achieve this.

The design specification

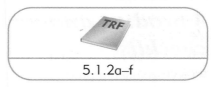
Having completed your **research** and **evaluated** all the information you have gathered, the next stage in the design process is to write a detailed **specification**.

Specification

The specification is one of the most important stages in the **design** process. The best specifications are clear, detailed and identify all the **criteria** needed for a product to be successful. It is usually written as a list.

The examples of student work below show how detailed specification points are built up following the **evaluation** of the research.

Specification checklist

The specification framework opposite can be used for any design project. To use it, simply answer each of the questions as they apply to your own project. Some of the headings may not always be appropriate and can be left out.

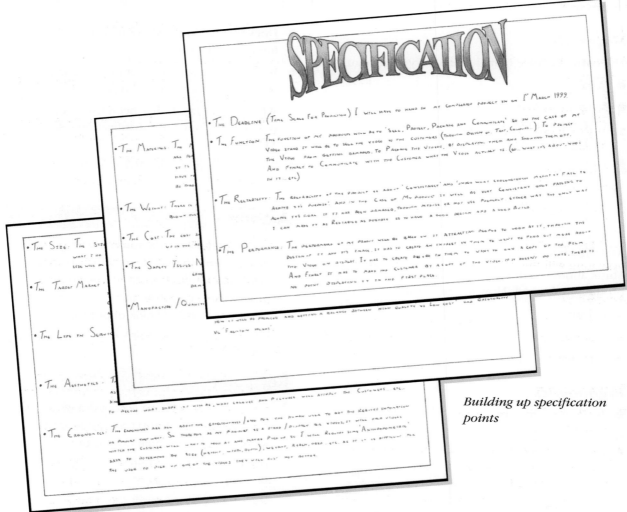

Building up specification points

Time scale for production (the deadline)

When do you have to hand in your completed project?

Function

What is the purpose of this design? What is it meant to do?

Reliability

- Under what circumstances might the project fail to achieve its **function**?
- How will you ensure that the product works as intended every time?

Performance

How and where is this design meant to work?

Size

Are there any specific dimensions to be considered?

Target market

- At which group of people are you aiming this design?
- What is their type, age, sex, interest, occupation, culture?
- What image should this design create?

Life in service

How long will this design be expected to last?

Aesthetics

How will colour, line, shape, texture, pattern, form and/or tone contribute to the visual appeal of this design?

Ergonomics

- What effect should this design have on its human user?
- What **anthropometric** data – information on the human body in terms of height, width, weight, reach, grip, angle of vision and range of movement – will you need to use in this design?

Materials

- Which materials would be suitable to use for this design?
- What qualities do they need to possess (e.g. weatherproof, rustproof, fireproof, easy to clean, difficult to scratch, reflective, flexible, strong, lightweight, cheap, heat resistant, opaque, transparent, biodegradable, etc.)?

Weight

- Are there any specific weights to be considered?
- Does it matter if this design is light or heavy?

Safety

What safety factors are important in this design?

Cost

Do you have to design to a budget?

Manufacture/quantity

- How will this design eventually be produced and in what quantities?
- Write in detail about the possible conflicting demands you may face. For example:
  - high quality versus low cost
  - originality versus fashion trends.

Activity

1 Using the specification framework on this page, write a detailed specification for a **point of sale** display used to promote a new film of your choice.

Key points

- A product specification is a list of the key features that the intended product should possess. Each specification point should be a performance target that the product should meet.
- The specification should not prescribe the product, for example it should not say it must be blue and made from **acrylic**.

Design ideas

Design ideas are the first thoughts you have about a solution to a problem. They are usually initial **sketches** and are often incomplete solutions. For this reason designers often call these first ideas design roughs or 'rough visuals'. These initial ideas do not need to be a work of art – examination boards expect you to get lots of ideas down quickly. Remember this motto:

'Designing is thinking on paper.'

Let your ideas grow

Within the initial idea stage of a project the main requirement is that you should produce a range of suitable ideas. In examination terms, a range is always more than three. It is often a good idea to try and break down the problem into smaller pieces and then bring all the bits together as the ideas develop.

For example when working on a new **corporate identity** for a company you could start by looking at the **logo** and then consider text styles and layout before moving on to product design such as packaging. In this way, the product develops naturally and the problem is more manageable.

Choosing a design

When you have created a range of different ideas, it is important that you start to make decisions about which designs to use and which ones to reject. These decisions should always be recorded on your design sheets and the decisions must be made by **evaluating** the ideas against the **specification**. Use your design specification as a checklist as you go through.

One of the key features of GCSE projects is that the product you design should be able to be manufactured in quantity. This means that as your thoughts develop and grow you must consider how your ideas could be made commercially.

Putting design ideas down on paper – rough visuals

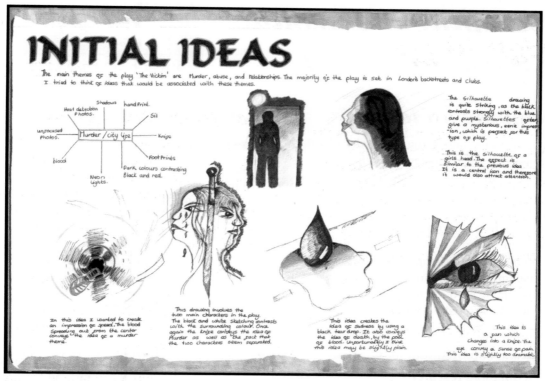

Some initial ideas

Communicating ideas

It is very important that you clearly communicate your ideas to others – this is an important design skill and it is known as the visual language of design. The most important thing to remember is that you must choose the most appropriate form of communication at different stages in the design process. Formal drawings should not be used at the initial design stage – they come later. When communicating your initial ideas you should always:

● use rough sketches and include notes (which explain your ideas and state how they meet the specification points)

● ignore the tiny details – these will come through in the development

● think small, then grow

● produce a wide range of initial ideas (rough visuals) – don't just draw three complete solutions and then choose one

● use a blow up of a feature if you need to show detail.

Activity

1 Sketching ideas quickly takes practice. Take ten minutes to produce a minimum of five sketches for each of the activities listed below:

   a Sketch ten uses for a paper clip or clips.

   b Design a logo for 'super flight' airlines.

   c Sketch five uses for an old shoe.

   d Design a fold-up toothbrush.

Key points

● A range of ideas means at least three.

● Rough sketches are more important than beautiful solutions at the early stages of design.

● Communication is the visual language of designers.

● Always use notes to evaluate your ideas against the specification.

Developing the product for manufacture 1

Developing an idea

The **development** stage is the stage where initial ideas are taken a stage further in an effort to improve them and develop a better solution. This stage is sometimes called the 'synthesis' or bringing together of ideas. It is not just a paper exercise that can happen through further sketching – ideas must be tested and evaluated by making models and computer images. To achieve maximum success in this stage you will need to use the five-point checklist for development below. Ask yourself if you have:

1 combined the best parts of the first ideas

2 refined and improved your ideas

3 carried out more **research**

4 make simple **mock-ups** (models to test ideas)

5 **evaluated** your ideas against the **specification**?

Looking at a developed idea

When you look at a final idea, you should be able to trace it right back through a project to see where the first germ of the idea started.

Look at these four pages from the development stage of a GCSE student's coursework. They show how an initial idea (below) was developed and tested and grew towards a final solution. The project involved the design of a series of posters and associated merchandise for a murder mystery play entitled 'The Victim'.

By applying the five-point development checklist, you can see that the student has produced a high quality graphic product that successfully meets the **criteria** identified in the original design specification.

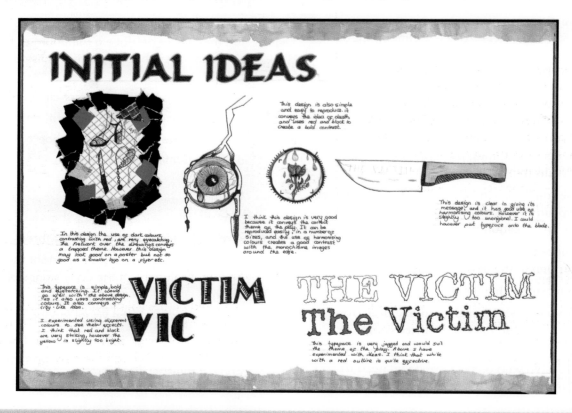

The idea evolves ...

Once an idea has been formed, you can begin to create high quality products by using ICT modelling. In the work to the right, the original drawing of an eyeball idea is scanned into the computer and loaded into a design program. In this way, colours, backgrounds and different typefaces can be tested and modelled easily.

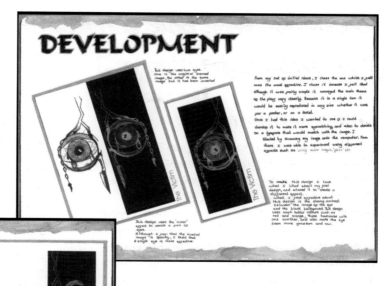

Further development takes place using ICT. The original **scanned** image is able to be distorted using different computer effects. The images are printed out and evaluated in the annotations next to the ideas on the page. Different colour testing and typefaces are tried.

Development continues. A lens effect is placed over the eyeball. The student evaluations show that the solution is now well developed. The student models examples of the tickets to see how the **logo** will work on an actual graphic product. A fully developed logo starts to emerge – further developments are recorded by the student.

Activities

1 Give two reasons why it is important to evaluate your ideas against the design specification.

2 Why is it important to carry out further research during design development?

Key point

- It should be possible to carefully trace the development of a final solution all the way through the design **portfolio** – right from the initial idea through the development stage into the realization stage.

Developing the product for manufacture 2

Using mock-ups

It is important to test out your ideas by using **mock-ups** or **development** models. Paper, card or any appropriate materials should be used to see what the product will look like in 3D. In this way, the form and function of the products can be more effectively **evaluated**. Even the most basic models should be included within your **portfolios** for assessment.

Developing the idea with manufacture in mind

Another key requirement of the development stage is that you should consider the commercial manufacture of the graphic product you are designing. When products are manufactured commercially, it is very important that they are all of a consistent (the same) quality. Tests are made by manufacturers to ensure that this happens. Within assessment objective 4 of the OCR **specification**, you are asked to produce a system to ensure that an identical batch of 50 products can be made.

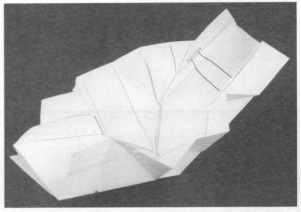

Ideas for graphic products are tested using simple mock-ups.

Stencils

Stencils can be easily cut from thin card or plastic. They are particularly useful for batch production of your final design. By using a stencil, you can ensure consistent quality and accuracy.

Ensuring consistency

A good way to ensure consistency when making is to use a **jig** or **template**. There are many devices that can be used for this purpose, such as:

- stencils
- cutting jigs
- colour charts.

When a logo or pattern has to be repeated, a stencil is a useful way to ensure consistency

Cutting jigs

Cutting jigs are accurately made and enable exact sizes to be reproduced. They can be produced by hand or on the computer. Greater accuracy and consistency can be achieved by using a computer and computer-controlled cutter.

Using computer-aided manufacture (CAM)

A batch of 50 or more nets such as the point of sale display below can be quickly and accurately cut by computer-aided manufacture.

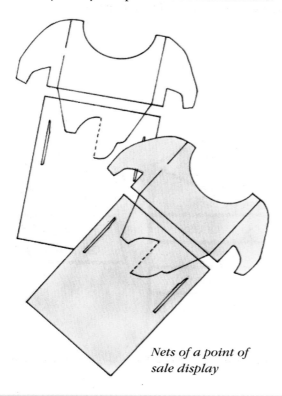

Nets of a point of sale display

Colour bars

When ICT is used in the development of an idea, design software usually allows you to apply printer's marks to a design. Printer's marks are used to test for quality. One such mark is a colour bar. A colour bar is a visual means of checking the colour quality of the printout against the original colours required.

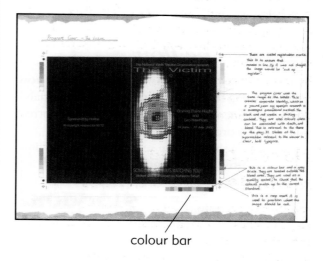

colour bar

The colour bars are attached to the printout using design software. The colour bars allow you to test for quality over time.

Activity

1 Give two ways that will enable you to ensure consistency when making a batch of 50 graphic products in a school design and technology room.

Key points

● Always use the five-point checklist (see page 28) to help you achieve maximum marks in this assessment objective.

● Use **mock-ups** as part of the development. Successful development of an idea can rarely be achieved simply by using a pen and pencil.

Planning the make 1

Before you make your product you need to plan the order of manufacture and the processes, tools and equipment to be used. Producing a time plan will help you to keep on target.

Go with the flow

When you produce a plan, you have to show how you are going to manage the necessary materials, tools, equipment and other resources in the correct sequence in order to make the product. One simple way of showing the sequence of production is to use a **flow chart** diagram (see below).

The flow chart places the processes that need to be carried out into the correct sequence and uses arrows to indicate the direction of the flow of work. The advantage of a flow chart is that it gives a quick visual indication of the plan.

In order to make flow charts more consistent, a series of standard symbols (flow chart symbols) are used.

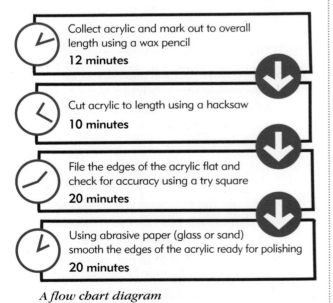

A flow chart diagram

Flow chart symbols

Flow charts are extremely useful when planning any process and can determine the critical path – the sequence of operations that will control the outcome of the process.

The flow chart symbols graphically communicate the different processes that are carried out in order to manufacture a product.

The enlarged version of the flow chart opposite shows how feedback and control operations can be demonstrated. Whenever a decision needs to be made that will result in a yes or no answer, a loop is put into the system. If the answer to the question is no, the operation is carried out again with adjustments added. The flow chart shows that the operation continues looping around until the answer to the question is yes – the flow chart then carries on.

In this way the system becomes **closed loop**, or a system that has built-in feedback. Whilst flow charts are a useful way of communicating the plan of work and sequence of operations, they have the disadvantage of lacking the detailed information that is often needed for production. Also, because manufacturing products is often a complex process, flow charts can become very long winded.

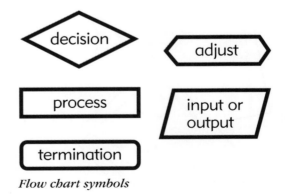

Flow chart symbols

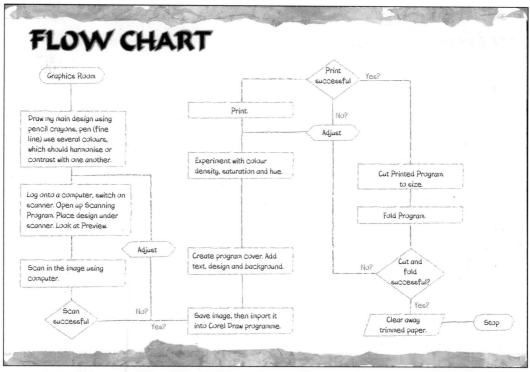

An example of how a student has used flow chart symbols to graphically communicate the different processes

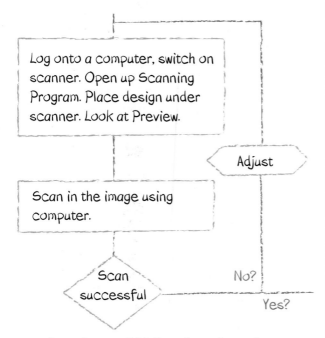

An enlarged part of the flow chart shows that feedback and control loops can be added

Activities

1 List two positive features of a flow chart when used to illustrate a process.

2 Draw a flow chart for making a cup of tea.

3 Using the example of a flow chart for producing a cup of tea, explain what is meant by feedback loop.

4 Using a computer program of your choice, draw a flow chart for producing a compliments slip.

Key points

- Flow charts are a good way of showing the path or route of a process. They use standard symbols which are readily understood and include feedback loops.

- Flow charts are a useful way of visually showing the planning for manufacture, but they lack the detail required for full manufacture.

Planning the make 2

Producing a schedule

Planning is important because it helps prevent mistakes and makes good use of your time. Planning the manufacture of a graphic product takes practice. It is always a good idea to write each of the stages down in turn. When you allocate times to a process and state how all the resources needed are to be used, the plan becomes a production schedule.

Production schedules contain much more information than **flow charts**. They have **quality control** and **quality assurance** procedures and checks built into them to ensure that the objective of producing a high quality graphic product is achieved.

The key features of a production schedule

Blank production schedules are usually pre-printed on a **grid** which can then be filled in by production controllers for the particular product that is being made. Grids are an extremely useful way of producing production schedules. They save time and enable the detailed information to be added.

The blank production schedule can be pre-printed and filled in separately for each graphic product being produced.

Each production schedule contains the following headings:

● *Stage/task* – a brief description of the process to be carried out.

● *Tools, materials and processes to be carried out* – this should list the resources needed for each stage.

● *Accuracy required* – this states how close to the actual size you are prepared to accept (this is called **tolerance**).

● *Time needed* – an accurate forecast of the time required to complete the task.

Stage or task	Tools, materials, processes to be undertaken	Accuracy required	Time needed, deadline	Quality assurance procedures	Alternative methods of manufacture	Safety – risk assessment

A production schedule grid

PRODUCTION SCHEDULE

Stage/Task	Tools, Materials & Processes to be Undertaken.	Accuracy required	Time needed/ Deadline.	Quality Assurance Procedures	Quality Control Procedures.	Alternative Methods of Manufacture	Safety.
Create Setup of Cover.	Enlarge the image. Add a background. and written information.	make sure text is clear and easily legible. Scaling must be accurate	1hr	Measurement tools. use zoom to focus in on written text. - check spelling, typeface used etc.	Visual checks - compare with the original and the tickets already created for continuity.	Draw and create by hand. Use a different software system.	Safe.
Printing.	use inkjet Printer, and Photo finish glossy paper (A4). load Paper. Adjust printer settings.	check that this type of paper is only loaded one sheet at a time. check that glossy side is the correct way up.	10 - 20mins.	Use crop marks registrations marks to keep design in line on the photo plate. use colour bar and grey scale	Visual checks against original to ensure continuity use densitometer to check quality of the colour.	use a different printer eg Laser bubble jet. use ordinary card.	Ensure printer is properly connected. that the printers voltage matches the outlet voltage. Keep fingers away from print head.
Production of The Victim Poster - Small aquire Image	Select image used in other products and import into a new document. Draw a new Poster using box tool.	Make sure image is recognisable and has visual continuity with other products.	10 - 20 mins.	use zoom tool to make sure lines are straight. Clear any blemished areas using a fuzz tool.	Make sure original is saved so changes can be made if needed.	use image from Clipart on all products instead.	Safe.
Fit image to size.	Shrink image to A4 size. Or use Scales and rulers on Corel Draw. Add text.	Very accurate scaling. Poster must fit exact width of point of Sale display	½ hr.	use Measuring scale on Corel Draw contouring of text and images.	Visual checks. Save original.	Create by hand. Print out clipart images and stick onto Poster size.	Safe. - as long as pr computer is being used correctly.
Printing.	Print onto A4 paper cut to size if needed afterwards.	crop marks 12.5mm outside bleed area.	20 mins	Grey scale Colour bar Crop marks.	Visual checks against original Densitometer checks on quality of colour.	Create by hand.	Keep fingers away from printer head. Printer must be properly connected.
Production of The Victim Sale Display unit.	Import net onto Corel Draw from floppy disk.	make sure net is correct size. All cut and fold lines are clear.	10 - 20 mins.			trace net onto card then create it. Draw image/Design onto it.	Safe.
Create Sale Display unit Set up.	Add colour, text. import image used on other products.	make sure text is the Same as with previous products. Image is not to large nor to small	1hr.	Check that colour density is constant. use zoom tool to adjust details.	Visual check against other products.	Draw a colour design onto photo copied net.	Safe.
Printing.	Print using A3 printer A3 card.	make sure printer is Set to 'quality' to make sure product is high quality	10 - 20mins.	crop marks 12.5mm outside bleed area grey scale, colour bar registration marks.	Visual check against other products to check for continuity. Densitometer for colour accuracy.	Photocopy net. colour design onto it.	Keep fingers clear of print head. Printer must be properly connected.
cut and fold	Scissors for scoring with ruler	Score gently. Cut carefully folds 0.8mm +/-	10 - 20 mins.	Take time - ensure sharp scissors for accurate cutting	Visual checks. Print more if unhappy	Print until happy with result. use guillotine.	Care when handling scissors.

An example of a student's production schedule

- *Quality assurance* – a statement about how you are going to make sure that mistakes will be avoided.

- *Quality control* – how you are going to check the accuracy and quality of the product.

- *Alternative methods* – the alternative ways of making if things go wrong.

- *Health and safety* – the hazards involved in the process.

Production schedules, such as the example opposite, set realistic deadlines and identify critical points in the process where decisions have to be made or quality control checks added. A schedule like this helps you to plan your time accurately, so that you are not kept waiting for long periods for one stage to be completed.

Activities

1 Using a computer, produce a grid that can be used as a pre-printed production schedule.

2 Give three reasons why production schedules are important to the designer.

3 What is meant by the phrase critical points, and why is it important to identify these in a production schedule?

Key point

- Detailed production schedules can be produced with the aid of pre-printed grids. These grids identify all the key requirements for a schedule and state how quality is going to be ensured.

Putting quality first

What is quality?

We all know what we mean when we talk about quality, but it is hard to define. The *Oxford English Dictionary* defines it as: 'the mark or standard of excellence'. So, quality is about achieving the highest possible standards in all **design** activity.

Quality versus cost

Achieving the highest quality often means having to spend more. For example, magazines are produced to a higher print quality than newspapers. The pictures are clearer, the paper is heavier, stronger and glossy, but magazines are more expensive to produce.

Newspapers are printed on a very cheap, absorbent paper called newsprint. The pictures in newspapers are not very crisp because the printing is not as high a quality as a magazine.

The glossy magazine is of a much higher quality than the newspaper

Working to a tolerance

What is your level of acceptance? How much are you prepared to put up with? These questions are about defining standards and quality. Whenever a product is manufactured, a **tolerance** is set. Tolerance is the acceptable amount that the finished product varies in size or quality from a perfect standard.

Tolerances are usually specified in a manufacturing **specification** which is given to the printer. For example, if A4 paper is required, the tolerance might be:

'The paper used should be A4 90**gsm** white paper 210 x 297 +/– 0.5mm.'

This says that the maximum tolerance on paper size is the range 210.5 to 209.5 mm wide and 297.5 to 296.5 mm long. Providing the finished paper size is within these limits, the tolerance has been met. All products have tolerances set for them and they form the basis for the quality checks that follow.

Quality assurance and quality control

When a large number of graphic products are being made, it is important that the standard of quality is the same on each one. This is very important because otherwise the customers will be unhappy and the manufacturer will lose money. The customer expects to get good value for money from a quality product. The manufacturer needs to make the products as efficiently as possible with little or no waste. In order to achieve quality, the manufacturer uses **quality control** and **quality assurance** techniques.

Quality assurance

Quality assurance (QA) is like a guarantee of quality written by the manufacturer. QA is a series of checks and procedures that are followed at every stage of the making to ensure that failure or poor quality goods are prevented.

European quality assurance standards such as ISO 9000 are awarded to companies that are able to guarantee a consistent quality of product or service.

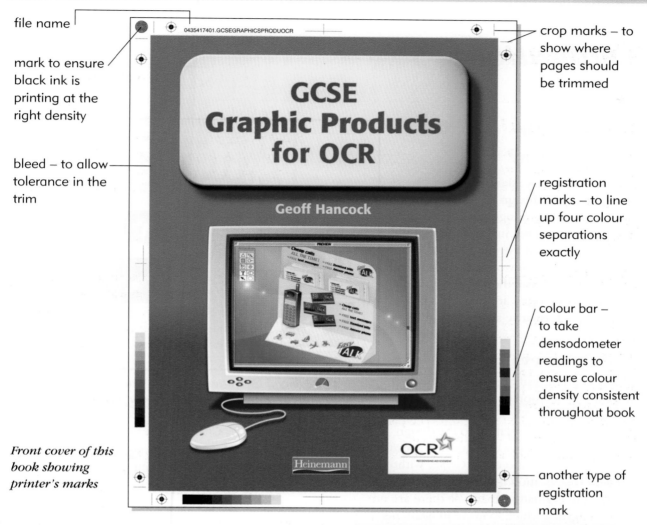

file name

mark to ensure black ink is printing at the right density

bleed – to allow tolerance in the trim

crop marks – to show where pages should be trimmed

registration marks – to line up four colour separations exactly

colour bar – to take densodometer readings to ensure colour density consistent throughout book

another type of registration mark

Front cover of this book showing printer's marks

Quality control

Quality control is used to check that the products produced meet the required quality standard. This means making a series of checks for things like colour and size. Graphic products that are printed use a series of printer's marks for quality control. For an example of this, look at the picture above, which shows the types of printer's marks that were used in the production of this book.

In practice, quality control would be too time consuming if every product was individually inspected. In most **systems**, a sample such as one in every 100 products are inspected. In this way, the risk of failure is reduced. If the products are found to be acceptable, production is allowed to continue.

Activities

1 Explain why quality is important for:
   a the manufacturer
   b the consumer.
2 Explain, giving one example, what is meant by the term tolerance.

Key points

- Quality control involves checks that are carried out on a product or its components after they have been manufactured.
- Quality assurance is the procedures that are put in place to reduce the risk of failure during manufacture.

Evaluation

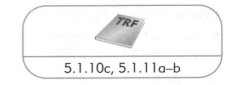

What is an evaluation?

Evaluation means asking questions about how well **design** ideas or the final product meet the design **specification**. The evaluation is not just something that occurs right at the end of a project. The very best coursework has evaluation at different stages all the way through. This is because there are two types of evaluation – formative and summative.

Formative evaluation

This is ongoing and occurs every time you make a decision or judgement about your work. These judgements should be made in relation to the design specification. That is why a detailed specification is so important to success at GCSE. Without a detailed specification it is impossible to have meaningful evaluations because there are no **criteria** against which to make judgements.

Summative evaluation

This occurs at the very end of the project. It specifically judges how well the final 'made' product meets the specification.
It should include proposals for further development of the product or improvements to the manufacturing system to improve quality. There are do's and don'ts for good evaluations:

Do:

- Answer every point on the specification.
- Write in the third person (never say things like 'I think that …').
- Include **sketches** of how to improve the product.

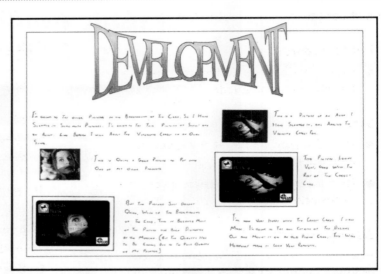

Design ideas should be evaluated by annotating them. Ideas should be judged against how well they meet the requirements of the design specification

- Get an opinion from someone other than you – ideally the client or a member of the product's **target market**.

Don't:

- Write a diary of how you got on.
- Give opinions that you cannot prove by testing.

A summative evaluation checklist

Use the framework that follows to structure your evaluation. This will link exactly to the design specification (see page 25 for specification checklist). Simply answer each of the questions in turn and relate them to your product. Remember – you don't have to use all of these headings. Some of them may not be relevant to your project.

Production time scale (deadline)

- Have you managed to complete the project by the deadline? If not, what are the reasons?

Function

- Does this design do the tasks it should?

Performance

- How well does this design work in the places for which it is intended?

Size

- How does this design fit any specified dimensions?

- How is the size of this design appropriate to its **function**?

Target market

How have you made this design attractive to the group of people for whom it is intended?

Maintenance

- How have you ensured that this design can be kept in good working condition?

- How are you able to keep this design clean?

- Is it easy to repair or clean?

Life in service

- How have you ensured that this design will last for its intended life span?

Ergonomics

- How does this design affect its human user?

- What **anthropometric** data has helped you make decisions whilst designing?

- What decisions did you make and how have these decisions affected the outcome?

Materials

- Why have you chosen these materials for your designs? (You may have made a **prototype** in different materials to those intended for the final product.)

- Evaluate your choice of materials for your intended final product. What are the advantages of these materials? What are the disadvantages of these materials?

- Would any other materials be equally appropriate or better?

Safety

- What precautions have you taken to ensure that the design is safe to use?

Cost

- How have you managed to keep within your budget?

Manufacture/quantity/quality

- Have you chosen the most appropriate printing or making process to produce the design prototype in sufficient quantities?

- Have you taken into account efficient use of time, labour, energy and materials? How successful was your system at ensuring quality?

Activity

1 Using the evaluation checklist, write a summative evaluation of a product of your choice.

Key points

- Evaluations occur at every stage of the design process.

- Evaluations are critical judgements made against the design specification.

- The decisions taken during evaluations should be based upon evidence and not just your own opinions.

- The best evaluations include opinions from people other than the designer – preferably the person for whom the product was designed.

Costing graphic products

Working to a budget

When developing a **design specification** for a new graphic product, it is important from the start to realise that **designers** always have to work to a budget. Every decision that you make will be influenced by cost. The quality of materials, the cost of production and the number required will all determine the cost of the final product. Whenever you design anything, remember this saying:

'Everything has its price and when faced with two very similar products, the customer will usually choose the cheaper one.'

The quality and content of a product will have a great influence over the retail cost of a product. A newspaper is made from cheaper newsprint and printed in black and white. The quality of the materials and production processes used for a magazine is much superior, and this is reflected in the price.

Specifying the product and detailing the cost

When a designer is given a new graphic product to design, the production costs will always be taken into account. There is no such thing as an unlimited supply of money. Designers must work to a fixed budget when producing designs for manufacture or printing. For this purpose a detailed product specification is often drawn up.

The product specification will specify time, costs and special details (needed in production). Projects can sometimes go over budget by taking longer than the specified time to complete. Designers often have to make very difficult choices between the final cost and the time spent and the quality of materials.

The costs of promotion

Each year, billions of pounds are spent by companies on the production of a wide range of graphic products used to advertise their products. **Advertising** or promotional campaigns are carefully costed and budgets are set. The most appropriate graphic products that can be afforded are used.

A typical large manufacturing company may spend as much as £6 million on the designing and producing of display materials. Of this, £3 million may be spent on cardboard boxes, price tags, tissue paper and leaflets. The remainder will be spent on display boards and **point of sale** materials.

Projects can sometimes go over budget because of designers missing deadlines

A large point of sale display costs around £50.00. An A4 show card costs about £3.00, including packing and dispatch.

The creative services and **marketing** departments negotiate the size of the budget with the manufacturing company. These two departments work together to design the materials that will advertise the company products. The size of the budget determines printing decisions, such as whether to print in two colours or four, as well as such things as the paper size and quality. Sometimes freelance designers are used to help with aspects of the design. (Freelance means people who are self employed and whose services are hired by the company).

Requirements such as photographs and illustrations are usually produced by freelance photographers and designers.

The table below gives some idea about the cost of producing graphic products.

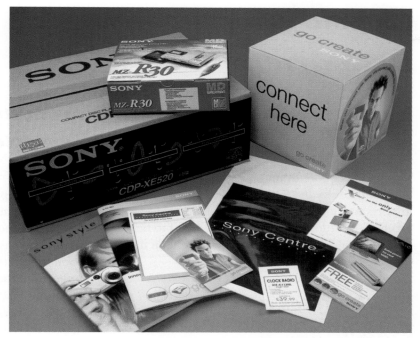

Large companies may spend as much as £6,000,000 per year on promotional graphic products

	£ average
Designing per hour	30–50
Photography per day:	
Fashion	2000
Product	1000
Illustration per drawing	1000

Printing (includes paper) per 10,000 two-sided A4 copies	
2 colour	600
3 colour	900
full colour	1200
stapling per 1,000 books	15
binding per 1,000 books	20
Stationery, graphic materials per project	100

Activity

1 Explain why the choice of materials and processes will have a great influence on the final cost of the product.

2 Explain why cost must always appear in a design specification for a graphic product. Use two examples in your answer.

Key points

- The cost of designing and producing commercial graphic products should be carefully considered in the design specification.

- The cost of producing graphic products is a major constraint on the designer.

- Research into the relative costs of materials and production processes will take place during the design development stage.

Classic graphics – Dr. Martens

'Between two products equal in price, function and quality, the better looking one will outsell the other.'

This famous quote from the renowned designer Raymond Loewy in 1929 emphasises the importance of the image and appearance of a product. By studying **designs** considered to be classics, you can learn much about the elements of successful design.

What makes a classic design?

A classic design is one that stands the test of time; it is one that transcends (rises above) fashion, one which combines image, quality and innovation. One such classic is the Dr. Martens 1460, a plain boot that from modest beginnings now sells one million pairs per month throughout the world.

On 1 April 1960, the first pair of Dr. Martens boots was made in a small factory in Northamptonshire. The manufacturer was R. Griggs and Co Ltd and the boots were named the now-famous '1460' to mark the date that they were made.

From anarchy to respectability – an image is born

It was the explosion of a new youth culture in the 1960s that signalled the rise of the Dr. Martens brand. With music and fashion the natural means of communication, Dr. Martens soon found itself recognized as the official uniform of the aggressive young male. From the Mods of the 1960s, to the skinheads of the 1970s, punks, Indies, grunge looks of the 1980s and 1990s, it is a street 'cred' that exists to this day. The late 1980s also saw the emergence of a huge market for girls footwear as Dr. Martens became a 'must have' fashion accessory.

Establishing the brand

Central to the success of the Dr. Martens **brand identity** has been the company's corporate image. Some of the key features of the product are encompassed within the corporate **logo**. The words 'Dr. Martens' are arranged in the shape of a boot while the word 'Martens' incorporates the famous grooved sole edge.

The Dr. Martens logo is a strong image

Dr. Martens '1460' boot – a classic design

Colour contrast is created through the use of black and yellow and once again draws on the heritage of the company's classic product line by incorporating the company's yellow stitch. This ensures that if photocopied, the image will remain strong. The use of the 'AirWair' bouncing ball logo emphasises one of the key properties of the classic product, the bouncing air-filled soles.

Developing the brand image

Central to any successful product is the ability to communicate to customers the factors that make the product different. Dr. Martens dramatized this difference in 1997 when the company introduced the 'Made like no other shoe on earth' slogan. This key consumer message more than met the company's objectives and lies at the heart of the Dr. Martens brand strategy.

The Dr. Martens slogan lies at the heart of the company's brand strategy

The main **target market** remains the same for the classic 1460 eight-eyelet boot. This is constantly communicated through the **advertising** which shows images of the target audience. The use of such images reinforces the brand's identity within the chosen target market. Having established a strong market position for the brand, Dr. Martens created new markets building upon the reputation for established quality. Individual products targeted at women and children help to create a broader market appeal.

Building upon success

Part of the brand diversity strategy lay in the selective development of clothing and accessories which began in the early 1990s and is now a significant factor in the company's continued success.

A Dr. Martens accessory

Dr. Martens has been recognized as one of the world's top 100 brands, an image which the company proudly cherishes.

Activity

1 Think of a classic graphic design. Decide why it is a classic and what makes it successful. Using the Internet, research its history. Then produce an A3 sheet which outlines the history of the product.

Key points

- The Dr. Martens brand successfully communicates to its chosen target markets.
- The brand identity has been carefully produced and reflects the aims of the company.
- At the heart of the **corporate identity** is a an effective logo that endorses the company's diverse range of products.

Classic graphics – Walkers crisps

Walkers crisps – a brand leader

*'Dramatize relevant differences.
Dramatize a market property.
Create a difference.'*

These three key features of any successful brand's **marketing** strategy are clearly evident in the rise of the Walkers brand as a market leader. In the overcrowded crisp market, Walkers with its strong graphic identity and focus on quality stands head and shoulders above its rivals.

From humble beginnings

Mr Henry Walker, a butcher, moved to Leicester in the 1880s and established with his son a business offering quality meat products.

The business prospered and the shop became a factory.

The turning point in the development of the Walkers product came during World War II (1939–45). Because of the shortage of food, meat was carefully rationed and the Walkers factory sold out each day at about 10 in the morning. Mr Walker pondered over how he could make better use of his premises and his eager workforce.

The solution was potato crisps, which were already enormously popular with the public. From this humble beginning, the public's love affair with crisps and Walkers began, and crisp manufacture was here to stay.

Building success

It is estimated that 11 million people eat a Walkers product every day. The Walkers **corporate identity** is now well established and like so many other leading brands uses an instantly recognisable **logo**.

Features of the logo

The logo is based upon simple contrasting primary colours. The red and yellow combination, used by some of the world's leading companies such as Shell and McDonalds, creates enormous impact. Red is a very aggressive colour and when used with a submissive colour such as yellow, really stands out. The bannered sun is simple and gives the impression that the Walkers brand has locked up all the warmth and freshness of the sun. The use of the third **primary colour** blue creates a 3D quality to the lettering and adds impact.

The effectiveness of the logo comes from its simplicity. The product styling is maintained even when additional graphics are applied to the package, as shown here.

The Walkers 'free books for schools' promotion

When running a promotion such as Walkers 'free books for schools', the basic principles of the graphic **design** are maintained. The 'free books' is held within a banner of the same shape and style. The colours used are consistent, and the use of blue to create 3D shadowing is also used. This helps to create **visual continuity** for the product, which links all the different graphic elements and improves the appearance of the product.

At home and abroad

As with all successful identities, the Walkers brand uses simple graphic devices and primary colours. They are easy to remember, are simple and clearly relate to the product. The simplicity of the design means that it can easily be transferred to other products. The Walkers brand is only

sold in the United Kingdom. However, the product itself is sold in Europe under the name Lay's. The design features of the Walkers logo easily translate to the Lay's brand.

This European brand shows how the simple effective design of the logo can be modified to suit a new and different market. Whilst retaining the essential features of the Walkers logo, Lay's has created its own **brand identity**.

Activity

1 Visit the Walkers website at: www.walkers.corpex.com/crl15p5/index.htm then answer the following questions:
   a What was the address of Walkers first shop?
   b How many people are employed at Walkers?
   c How many tonnes of potatoes do Walkers use each year?

Key points

- The Walkers brand uses the combination of yellow and red to create a very simple and effective logo. By creating a logo using simple graphic devices such as the sun and banner, it can be remodelled for use with other brands.

- Visual continuity is an important concept within graphic product design.

Questions

1 A company that produces wallpaper borders needs a display stand for promotional purposes. The **specification** for this product is given below.

The display stand must:

● be made from one piece of card

● hold three rolls (50 mm diameter x 120 mm high)

● have space for clear graphics

● be able to be folded flat for delivery.

Using a range of **sketches** with notes **design** a suitable display stand.

2 The picture below shows a sample of a wallpaper border.

a Which age is the product aimed at?

● 0–6 years

● 7–10 years

● 11–16 years

Give one reason for your choice.

b Name two sources of information that the designer of this wallpaper may have used during the development of this idea. For each of these two sources, explain how they may have been useful to the designer.

c The specification for this wallpaper might include:

● the wallpaper border must be 75mm wide.

Make a table like the one below and add four more specification points and reasons. The first specification has been done for you.

Specification point	Reason
the wallpaper border must be 75mm wide	so that the wallpaper can be used as a border

3 The wallpaper border shown above has been cut to a width of 75 mm with a **tolerance** of 0.5 mm.

a What is meant by the term **quality control**?

b Explain and give *one* example what is meant by the term tolerance.

c Explain why a manufacturer needs to ensure that its products are produced within set tolerances.

4 a One very important specification point for this product is the manufacturing cost. How could this cost be kept as low as possible so that the retail price of the wallpaper is competitive?

b List four other important costs involved in the design and production of a graphic product.

5 It has been said that:

'The designer's freedom is a limited freedom.'

What does this phrase mean in relation to the costs involved in design? Use two examples to explain your answer.

COMMUNICATING DESIGN

Tools and equipment

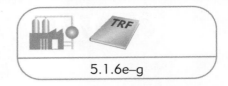

Designing and making high quality graphic products requires skill in the use of a range of tools and equipment. Choosing the right equipment is vital.

Drawing equipment

The common pencil is in many ways the designer's most important tool. The ability to draw and use a pencil for **sketching** through to accurate technical drawing is very important and there are different pencils for different tasks.

The hardness of the core is often marked on the pencil – look for a number (such as 2 or 3). The higher the number, the harder the writing core. You might see other markings on pencils. Some pencil manufacturers use the letter H to indicate a hard pencil. Likewise, a pencil maker might use the letter B to designate the blackness of the pencil's mark. The letter F is also used to indicate that the pencil sharpens to a fine point.

When sketching and shading, a soft pencil such as a 4B is used. When producing an **orthographic** drawing, a hard pencil that leaves a crisp **feint** line such as a 4H is used.

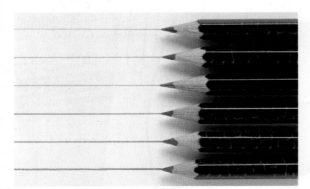

A range of pencils from soft (4B) that leave a heavy Black line through to Hard (4H) that leaves a crisp feint line

For further information about the history and uses of pencils look at the web site www.pencils.com.

Colouring pencils

Colouring pencils are useful for adding different shades of colour (**tone**). You can produce a darker tone simply by pressing harder. The tone is the amount of dark or light used. This is useful for shading.

The effect of light and shade can be shown by pressing hard with the coloured pencil

Fine line pens

Fine line pens with fibre tips are now popular with designers. They are useful for inking in lines and come in a variety of sizes. The most common sizes are 0.3 mm, 0.5 mm and 0.7 mm. The size relates to the thickness of the line the pen produces. Fine line pens leave a crisp black line and can be used for lines and text.

A sketch with the outlines 'inked in' using a fine line fibre tip pen

A presentation drawing rendered using a spirit marker

Spirit markers

One of the most useful ways of applying colour quickly to drawings in order to achieve a professional look is to use spirit markers. Marker pens are widely used by graphic designers for adding solid or uniform colour.

Drawing instruments

In order to produce accurate technical drawings a drawing board is usually used. Drawing boards often have a parallel motion rule attached to them. This is a straight edge that slides vertically up and down the surface of the board. By placing a set square against this rule various accurate angles or parallel lines can be drawn.

Set squares

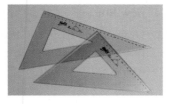

Set squares look like triangles. They are used for producing accurate drawings. One type has a 30-degree and 60-degree angle and is used for **isometric** projection. The other has a 45-degree angle and is used for **oblique** projection, **axonometric** projection and constructing orthographic projections.

Compasses and circle templates

Circles and arcs are drawn using a compass. Always use a compass with a screw adjuster for accuracy. (Compasses with fine line pen attachments can also be used.) For speed and ease of use, designers usually use **templates** for drawing circles and ellipses.

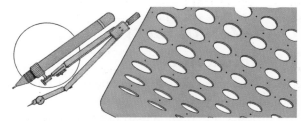

Compass with fine line attachment circle and ellipses template

Activity

1 Name the grade of pencil you would use for sketching and shading a picture. Explain your answer.

Key point

● There is a range of tools and equipment you can use when designing graphic products. You must select the right tool to create the effect you want.

Basic geometric shapes

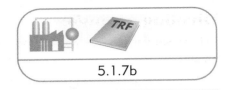
Being able to construct shapes accurately on paper is an important skill. The basic skills of geometry (constructing drawings using instruments such as the compass) will help you to draw any regular shape. Geometrical drawings take quite a long time to produce and are only used by graphic **designers** for final drawings and work such as accurately producing **nets/developments** for packaging such as Toblerone bars.

Useful geometry

Dividing a line

The first exercise is to divide a line of any length into two equal parts. When you divide a line you will produce a perpendicular. (This is a vertical line that is at right angles to the original line).

Draw a line of any length. Set your compass to more than half the length of the line. Place the point at one end and draw an arc.

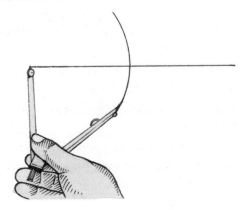

Repeat this by drawing an arc from the other end of the line. Now draw a perpendicular line that joins the crossing points of the two arcs.

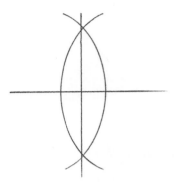

Dividing a line into any number of equal parts

A line of any length can be easily subdivided into as many equal parts as you wish using basic graphic equipment such as a compass, set square and ruler. Simply follow the three stages shown below for any number of equal divisions.

1 Draw a line of any length, then draw a new line at any angle to it. Set the compass to a size roughly equal to the number of divisions you want and mark along the new line.

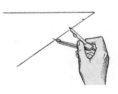

2 Draw a line from the last point on the angled line to the start of the original line using a ruler and a set square.

3 Now simply repeat this for all the divisions, making sure that all lines are at the same angle. You will need to hold the ruler or set square very steady at all times.

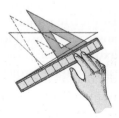

Dividing an angle

Using a similar process you can now subdivide an angle.

1 Draw any angle and then use a compass to draw an arc across the angle.

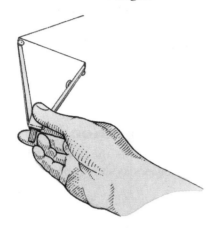

2 Draw two arcs from where the original arc crosses the angle. Now draw a line from the centre to where the new arcs cross.

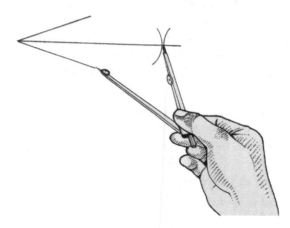

Constructing regular polygons

Once you can confidently bisect lines and angles you have learnt the basics of geometry. Now follow the stages listed below to accurately construct any regular shape from a given line (labelled AB).

Draw the given base, label it AB and divide it in half (bisect). Construct a square on AB. Join the diagonal from A and where it crosses the perpendicular line mark the point 4 (the number represents the number of sides of the shape).

Set the compass to the length AB and draw arcs from A and B in turn. Where these arcs cross on the perpendicular line, mark the point 6. Bisect the points 4 and 6 to find 5. The distance between 4 and 5 gives you the equal division for 7, 8, 9, etc.

To draw a pentagon (five-sided polygon) draw a circle from point 5, setting the compass at a length of 5B. Now simply adjust the compass to AB, then step off around the circle. All the remaining polygons can now be created using the same procedure.

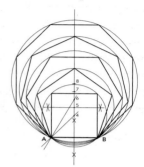

How to construct a polygon

Activities

1 Using notes and **sketches**, explain how a line of length 75 mm can be accurately divided into four equal divisions.

2 Draw an equilateral triangle (all angles must be 60 degrees) with a side length of 50 mm. Using the angle division method, construct 30 degrees and 45 degrees inside the triangle.

3 Construct a hexagon (six-sided polygon) with a side of length 40 mm.

Key points

● Basic geometry is useful for the accurate construction of working drawings, **templates** and final graphic products such as packaging.

● Perpendicular lines are drawn at right angles to the original line.

● Lines that cut a line in two are called **bisectors**.

● The basic equipment needed for geometry is a compass, ruler, set square and sharp 4H pencil.

Three-dimensional drawing 1

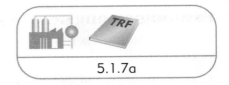
Pictorial drawing

Pictorial is the name given to the drawings that are in three dimensions (3D). Pictorial drawing methods are used to give a realistic impression of what a product will look like and are useful for explaining ideas to a client. This is particularly important when producing a drawing for a presentation . Consider the drawing below: is it sufficiently clear to gain a full appreciation of the product?

This 2D drawing does not show the form (3D view) of a product

If the toaster is now drawn in 3D it is more obvious what it is. The details of the product are more clearly communicated.

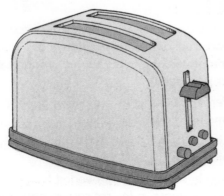

The 3D drawing represents the product more clearly than a 2D drawing

Three of the most useful pictorial drawing methods are:

- **isometric** projection
- **planometric** projection (see pages 54–5)
- **perspective** projection (see pages 56–9).

Isometric projection

In isometric projection, the horizontal lines are drawn at 30 degrees as shown below.

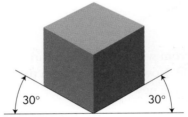

Isometric projection – draws horizontal lines at 30 degrees

As with all pictorial drawing methods, isometric projection shows three sides of an object. This gives a realistic impression of the object although isometric drawings can look a bit odd because your eye expects to see lines getting smaller as they go into the distance. Isometric drawings 'appear' to be getting bigger along their length.

Using a grid

A **grid** is useful for sketching in isometric projection. Isometric grids can be laid underneath your paper as a line guide.

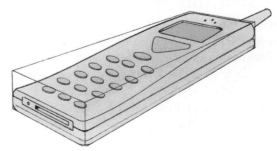

Using an isometric grid makes sketching quick and easy

Exploding your drawing

The finished product

A photograph or a drawing of a finished product gives a good representation, but it does not give any assembly instructions.

Pictorial drawing such as isometric projections can be used to show how the different parts fit together.

A drawing that shows all the different parts of a separated product is called an exploded drawing. When producing an exploded drawing, both the top and bottom parts should lie on the same vertical line.

An exploded view shows more details and gives an idea how the component parts fit together

Instructional drawings

Instructional drawings clearly describe a process or show how various component parts fit together without the use of words. These are invaluable for manufacturers who sell their products to different countries. Exploded drawings are particularly useful as instructional drawings because they can visually display a complicated or detailed process.

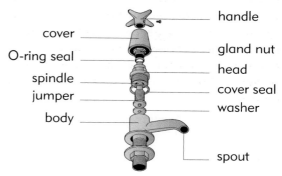

This complex drawing is produced on a computer and shows how all the various parts fit together

Activities

1 Using an isometric grid, sketch a cassette case in the closed position.

2 This drawing can now be used as an **underlay** for producing an exploded drawing. Using tracing paper, trace over the top half of the cassette case. Now, move the tracing paper up and trace through the bottom half. Now the basic drawing is produced, the detail can easily be added.

Key points

● Pictorial drawing methods are used because they give a more realistic impression of a product than 2D drawing.

● Isometric drawing is a method that draws horizontal lines at 30 degrees.

● Pictorial drawings such as isometric projection can be exploded and used as instructional drawings.

Three-dimensional drawing 2

Planometric drawing

Planometric drawing (often called **axonometric**) is a 3D method of drawing much favoured by architects and interior **designers**. This is because it is based upon an accurate 2D plan. An architect can look at plans and 2D drawings and visualize what the house or room will look like in his/her head, but a buyer might find it easier to understand if drawn in planometric projection.

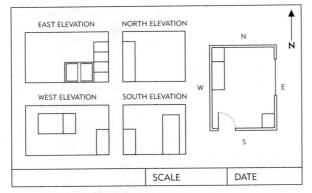

An architect's drawing of a room plan

The information in the plans can be used to make a planometric drawing. The plan is rotated through an angle of 30 degrees or 45 degrees, then details from the plan are added. All real-life verticals are shown as vertical lines and all lines are drawn accurately to **scale**.

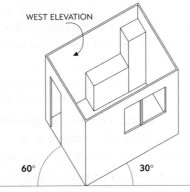

A planometric drawing of the room

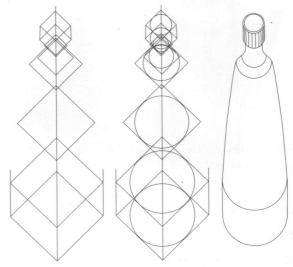

A planometric drawing of a bottle

Rules of planometric drawing

● The plan is true and drawn at an angle to the horizontal.

● All vertical edges stay vertical and must be projected from the plan.

● All measurements are true or are scaled equally.

One of the main advantages of planometric projection is that circles which are parallel to the plan can be drawn with a compass. This makes planometric drawings easier to construct. The view produced by a planometric drawing makes the designer look down at the object and gives a bird's eye view.

Crating

Drawing boxes or 'crates' is a useful staring point for drawing complex or detailed drawings. A crate goes around the outside of a product when it is being delivered to keep it safe. In the same way a crate is used to enclose a drawing using a method called **crating**.

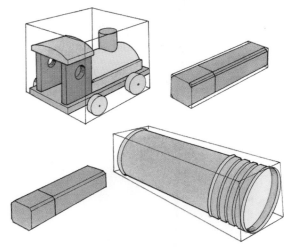

Once the detail has been added to a drawing the crate can be erased

Getting the proportion right

There is a saying used by designers, 'If it looks right, it is right'. This is not always true, but when it is applied to drawing it usually is. This saying is referring to proportion. Getting things in the right proportion is very important.

A good example of proportion is the human form. The height of an adult is usually eight times the length of his or her head. Look carefully at a range of common products. Would they look right if you changed their proportions?

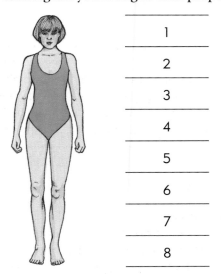

The height of an adult is usually eight times the length of his or her head

Making drawings stand out

To make a drawing stand out, designers use a variety of techniques to show the form of the object. The form is the object's 3D shape. One simple way of doing this is to use the thick and thin line technique.

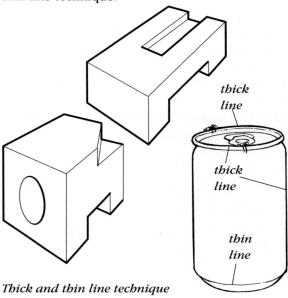

Thick and thin line technique

Thick and thin line technique

A simple way of applying thick and thin lines to an object is to imagine a spider walking over it. If a spider crosses over an edge and you can still see it, leave the line thin. If the spider disappears, draw the line about twice as thick.

Activity

1 Produce an accurate isometric drawing of a block pencil sharpener. Apply thick and thin lines to the completed drawing.

Key points

● Planometric drawing is used by architects and is produced by rotating a plan by 45 degrees and projecting the lines vertically.

● Thick and thin lines are a quick and easy way of making pictorial drawings stand out.

Perspective drawing 1

Take a look out of the window and really study the view. You will notice that objects near to you appear to be much larger than objects in the distance. This is because your eye puts things into **perspective**. This means that as objects get further away they appear to diminish (get smaller) in size until eventually they reach a point where they vanish.

Objects nearest the eye are in sharp focus and appear to be larger than those further away

The most realistic 3D drawings are made using perspective drawing techniques. There are several ways of producing perspective drawings. The most common types are single point and two point perspective.

Vanishing points and horizon lines

All perspective drawings have a **horizon line**. The horizon line separates the sky from the ground and helps to position the view of the object. The horizon line is the line of sight. The **vanishing point** or points are usually situated on the horizon line. This is the point where all lines meet on your drawing.

The horizon line and vanishing point

Single point perspective

When drawing in single point perspective the object can be drawn either above, below or on the horizon line. If the object is drawn above the line, the underneath is shown. If the object is drawn below the horizon line, the top surface is seen. If the object is drawn exactly on the horizon line, only the front surface is seen.

Sketching a lipstick case in single point

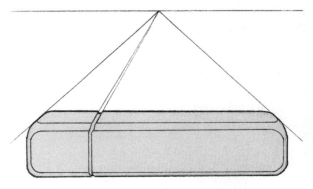

The lipstick container drawn in single point perspective above, below and on the horizon line

Remember that all lines must go back to the vanishing point.

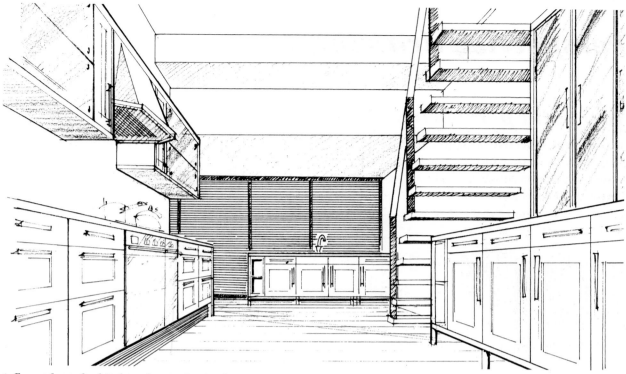

A floor plan of a kitchen drawn in single point perspective

Using single point perspective for interior design

Single point perspective can be very useful for showing the details of a room. The plan of a kitchen above is based upon a room that is 5 m wide × 4 m deep. The plan shows the relative positions of the units and worktops.

The vanishing point on a room plan is usually set at about 1.7 m high because it is the eye height of an average height adult.

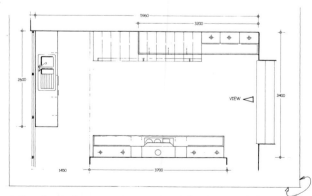

A final single point perspective drawing of the kitchen design

The vanishing point is set in the middle of the horizon line.

This type of drawing is very useful for showing a layout design to a client because it gives a good impression of what the final kitchen will look like.

Activity

1 You have been asked by an interior **designer** to create a detailed sketch of a new bedroom layout. Using single point perspective, design a new layout for a bedroom of your choice.

Key points

● With single point perspective the front face of the object is drawn 'flat' on the page.

● The object can be drawn above, below or on the horizon line.

● Single point perspective is particularly useful for showing the interior of a room.

Perspective drawing 2

Two point perspective

Two point **perspective** is an even more realistic form of pictorial drawing because it has two **vanishing points** which allow the viewer to see two sides of an object.

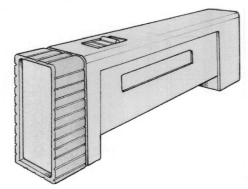

A rendered two point perspective of a torch

Sketching a stapler in two point perspective

1 Draw a **horizon line** above the centre of the page with vanishing points at each end. Draw a vertical line down to represent the front edge of the stapler.

Stage 1: drawing a stapler in two point perspective

2 Using **feint** construction lines, construct the crate for the stapler (see page 54). Remember to take all lines back to the vanishing points.

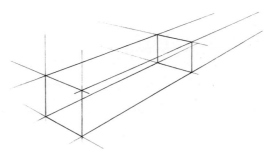

Stage 2: drawing a stapler in two point perspective

3 The final stage is to add the final detail. Complete each face of the crate in turn.

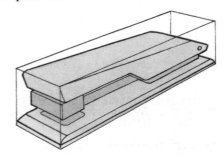

The final stage

Perspective circles

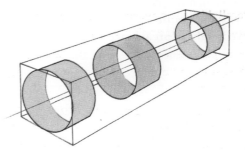

Circles in perspective

When drawing circles in perspective, a crate is drawn first. The centre of the box is found by joining the diagonals and the vertical and adding the horizontal lines. The four curves of the ellipse are then added (see page 66).

Perspective in action

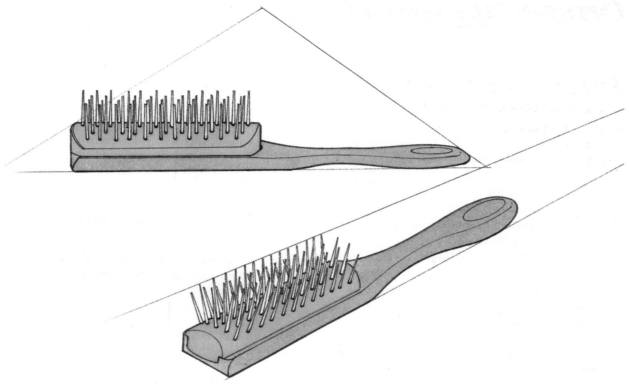

Perspective sketches for designs of a hairbrush

Rules of perspective drawing

There are some rules that will help you in perspective drawing. They are as follows:

- Parallel lines converge towards a vanishing point where they disappear.

- In single point perspective, the surface closest to the eye of the viewer is the only true view.

- In two point perspective, the vertical edge closest to the eye of the viewer is the only true length. All other dimensions are relative to it.

- If the chosen view has more than one vanishing point, they will be positioned on the horizon line which will always be horizontal.

Activity

1 Carry out a visual study of a ballpoint pen by producing a series of different views:

   a Produce three two point perspective views of the pen – above, below and on the horizon line.

   b For each view, change the position of the pen so that different perspective effects can be created.

   c Use colour to **render** each view and add thick and thin lines.

Key point

- Perspective drawing is the most realistic pictorial drawing method. That is because it represents what your eye actually sees – objects appear to get smaller the further away they are from you.

Orthographic projection

What is orthographic projection?

An **orthographic** drawing (projection) is a working drawing **designed** to provide all the information needed for someone other than the designer to make the product. Orthographic drawings have a visual language of their own. In order to read and fully understand an orthographic drawing you need to learn the signs, symbols and conventions used.

Unlike pictorial drawings, which always give three dimensions and an impression of what the product looks like, orthographic drawings view objects 'flat on'. That means they show each face in turn and are therefore two dimensional (2D).

Plans and elevations

Orthographic drawings have a language of their own. A view looking down on an object is called the plan. A view of either the front or the end is called an **elevation**.

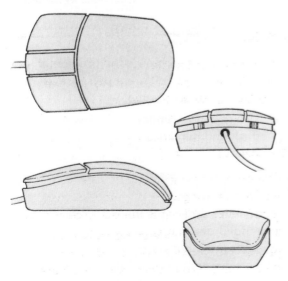

An orthographic drawing of a mouse

From 3D to 2D

A good way of understanding how orthographic projection works is to start by looking at a familiar object such as a video cassette.

A pictorial drawing of a video cassette

In order to produce an orthographic drawing, you have to imagine the product unfolded like a piece of packaging.

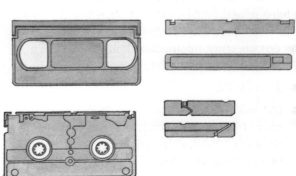

An orthographic drawing requires you to 'unfold' the product and draw each view separately

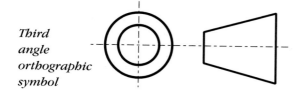

Third angle orthographic symbol

This type of layout is called third angle orthographic projection. With third angle, the view is drawn from where the eye is looking.

There is a standard symbol that appears on every drawing. This symbol shows that it is drawn in third angle.

The symbol shows an end elevation and front elevation of a cone with the top removed – the shape is like a lampshade. When you look into the cone you see a small circle, which is the hole in the top, and a large circle, which is the bottom edge.

Orthographic drawing in action

When all the different views come together, an orthographic drawing is produced. Orthographic drawings are precise, include all dimensions (measurements) and are drawn to scale.

The **scale** that the drawing uses must always be shown. In the drawing on the left, the scale used is 1:2. This means that the drawing is drawn half full size. Dimensions are always shown in millimetres and are usually **incremental**. This means that each new dimension follows from the last and is written separately.

Line types

Orthographic drawings are carefully drawn with a hard pencil such as 4H and often inked in with a fine line pen afterwards. The **feint** lines used to lay out the drawing are called construction lines. The other line types are:

● a centre line

● hidden detail – shows detail that cannot be seen. Hidden detail must be included on the drawing. The drawing to the left shows an orthographic drawing of a CD case. The small pivots that connect the two halves of the case together cannot be seen from the front elevation, but must be shown as hidden detail.

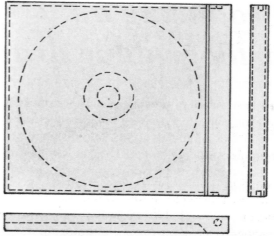

A third angle orthographic projection drawing of a CD case

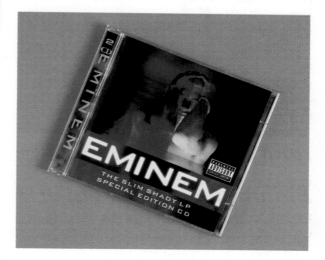

Activity

1 Produce a third angle projection of a floppy disc. Show the plan, front elevation and one end. Show all hidden detail.

Key points

● Orthographic projections are used as working drawings. They contain all the detail required for the product to be made.

● The best way of understanding how to produce an orthographic drawing is to think of a product folded out like a piece of packaging.

Producing an orthographic drawing

The best way of producing an **orthographic** drawing is to use a drawing board with either a T square or a parallel motion rule. Using this equipment, all lines will be straight and the top and bottom edges are drawn at right angles to one another.

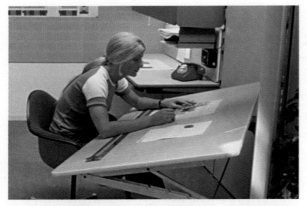

Equipment for producing an orthographic drawing

Planning the drawing

The first task is to decide which face of the object will be the front **elevation**. This will determine all the other views. Usually, the front elevation is the view that shows the most detail. To produce an orthographic drawing of this object, follow the four stages on the right.

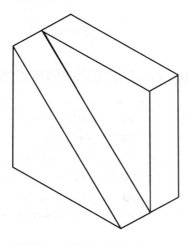

Stage 1 Plan the page

You need to ensure that there is enough room for all the views. It is usual to draw to front elevation in the middle of the page but be careful that there is room for the plan.

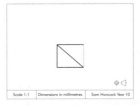

Front elevation is drawn first

Stage 2 Construct end elevation

Using the parallel rule and a 4H pencil, draw lines from each point on the front elevation towards the end elevation and the plan.

Construction lines drawn for end elevation and plan

Stage 3 Pencil in the end elevation

Carefully go over the end elevation with a 2H pencil.

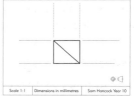

End elevation is pencilled in

Stage 4 Construct the plan

From a point exactly halfway between the front and end elevation, draw a construction line at 45 degrees. When the construction lines from the end elevation hit the 45 degree line, project the lines horizontally.

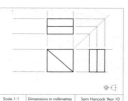

Plan is constructed using a 45-degree line

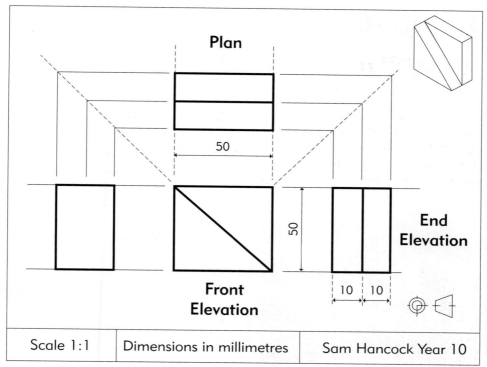

| Scale 1:1 | Dimensions in millimetres | Sam Hancock Year 10 |

Completed orthographic drawing

The final drawing

The final drawing includes all the dimensions (measurements). The dimensions are needed in order to make the object. In the final drawing a second end elevation is often added to make the drawing clearer.

Dimensioning

When adding the dimensions to the drawing there are clear rules that should be followed:

- The numbers should be placed above and in the middle of the dimension line.

- Dimension lines and projection lines should be about half the thickness of the object lines.

- Small filled arrows should be used.

- Only the absolute minimum dimension lines should be used.

There is a British Standard publication for orthographic drawing (BS 308; PD7308) which gives graphic designers all the correct symbols and procedures.

Activity

1 Look carefully at the pictorial drawings below. For each object produce a complete orthographic drawing (use dimensions to suit).

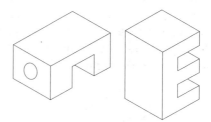

Key points

- To avoid running out of space, carefully plan where each elevation is going to go on the page before you start.

- Always use a hard pencil (minimum 2H) for producing orthographic drawings.

- The front elevation should be the view that gives the most detail about the object.

Sections and assemblies

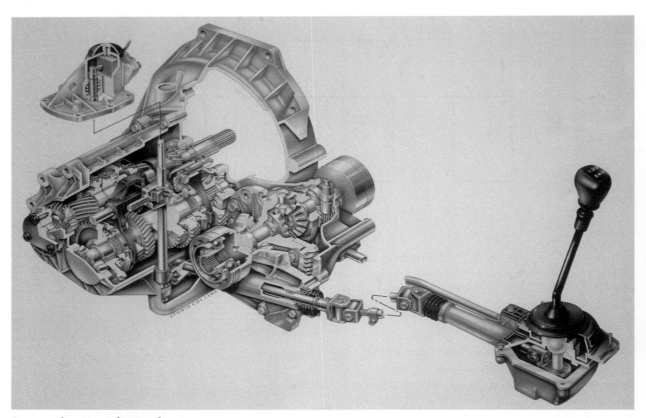

Section drawing of a gearbox

Showing all the details

Sometimes products are quite complex or contain parts that are difficult to show in **orthographic** drawings, even using hidden detail (see page 61). In these cases, a cut-through or **sectioned** drawing is produced.

Imagine taken a knife and cutting through the centre of an object and then drawing what you see. This is what a section drawing is.

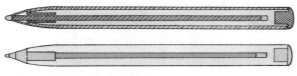

A front elevation and sectional view of a pen

Conventions for section drawings

Look carefully at the section drawing of the pen to the left. The sectional view shows what you would see if you cut along the centre line and looked in the direction of the arrows.

Section drawings use **hatched** lines drawn at 45 degrees to indicate the areas that have been cut. Areas that are not cut, such as a hole, are left blank.

Different parts of the product are represented by reversing the angle of the hatching. Unlike normal orthographic views, hidden detail is never included on sectional views.

Points to remember

Here are some helpful points to bear in mind when doing section drawings.

● Cut the object down the centre line and hatch any areas with lines drawn at 45 degrees using a set square.

● Try to keep your hatch lines as far apart as possible. In this way inaccuracies will be less obvious.

● Label the section line and the view, ensuring that the view conforms to third-angle projection (see page 60).

● Only produce a sectional view if a standard drawing does not provide sufficient detail for full understanding to be achieved.

Assembly drawings

Often products are made up from a number of parts, or components (such as nuts, bolts, screws, etc.). Orthographic drawings will often include a separate view of all the various parts joined together as well as details of all the individual components. This is known as an assembly drawing.

Assembly drawings should also include a parts list, so that individual components can be identified. The parts list will be numbered and details of materials, quantity and sizes will be given. Each individual component in the drawing is balloon referenced for identification. Balloon referencing means placing a number inside a circle. See the assembly drawing below for an example of this.

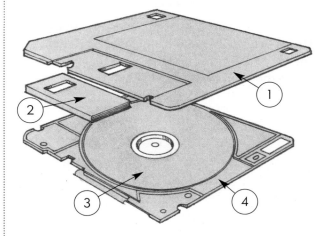

Part No	Description	Quantity
1	Outer Casing	1
2	Retaining Clip	1
3	Flexi Disc	1
4	Bottom Casing	1

An assembly drawing and parts list

Activity

1 Carry out a graphical study of a metal pencil sharpener. As part of the study you should complete:

a a front **elevation**, plan and two end elevations

b a sectional elevation of a pencil sharpener (do not hatch the screw used to fasten the blade to the body)

c an assembly drawing complete with parts list and full balloon referencing.

Key points

● Sectional views are added to orthographic drawings when additional detail must be given.

● Only those areas that are cut through must be hatched.

● Assembly drawings are always included as part of the working drawing, giving details of how the product is to be put together.

● Assembly drawings include a parts list that links to the numbers used in the balloon references.

Circles and ellipses

Circles explained

The circle is a very important geometric shape. The circle is a plane figure enclosed by a curved line called the circumference. The drawing below shows the main parts of a circle.

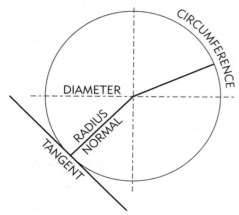

The main parts of a circle

Diameter – any straight line drawn through the centre of a circle and touching the circumference at both ends. The symbol for diameter is Ø.

Radius – any straight line from the centre of a circle to the circumference.

Tangent – a straight line which touches, but does not cut the circle. The exact point at which this line touches the circle is known as the point of tangency.

Normal – the radius from the centre of the circle to the point of tangency. The tangent is always perpendicular (at 90 degrees) to the normal.

When is a circle not a circle?

The answer is – when it's an ellipse! Imagine you are looking directly at someone sipping a can of fizzy drink. Look at the shape of the bottom of the can in the following diagrams.

Initially, only a very thin, flattened circle (ellipse) will be seen.

As more and more of the drink is consumed the ellipse will gradually become fatter.

As the can is brought to the horizontal the full shape of the circle is easily seen.

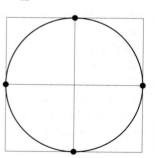

Axes and touch points

If you draw a square, then draw a circle that fits exactly inside it, you will notice that it touches the square in four places. Also, the circle has a vertical and a horizontal axis which are equal in length.

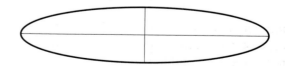

Because the ellipse is flattened, one axis is longer than the other. The longer axis is called the major axis and the shorter is called the minor axis.

Sketching an ellipse

30°

Firstly, **ghost** the crate for the ellipse in **isometric** projection. Find the centre of the crate by joining the diagonals

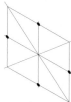

Draw in the two axes to find the four touch points.

Carefully join the four touch points with curves. Ghost the curves first until you get a curve that looks right.

This is an ideal way for quickly **sketching** relatively small ellipses. Accurate drawings take a little more time and effort.

More accurate curves

To produce more accurate curves you need more touch points on your circle. This is relatively easy to do, but you need a pair of compasses to divide the square into equal slices.

Draw a line at any angle to the square and use a set of compasses to mark off six equal divisions.

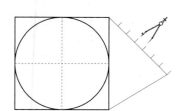

Join the bottom edge of the square to the last mark on the angled line. Next, join all the other marks on the line to the square with parallel lines.

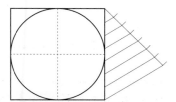

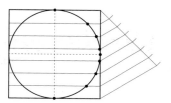

Now draw parallel lines across the box. Where these lines cross the circle are the new touch points.

By using this technique, you can produce accurate drawings. The drawing of the CD and case on the right shows how the touch points have been used to create the shape of the CD and its holder.

Activity

1 This drawing shows the front and side view of a battery. Find out the dimensions of a battery and using isometric projection produce an accurate drawing.

Key points

- An ellipse is a flattened circle which has a major and a minor axis. When sketching an ellipse, remember that it must touch at the same points as a circle.

- Ellipses have one long axis – the major axis – and one shorter one – the minor axis.

- Ellipses are easy to sketch once you have found the four touching points.

- When producing an accurate ellipse **designers** normally use pre-produced plastic **templates**, which are highly accurate and easy to use.

Signs and symbols

Getting informed

One of the key **functions** of a graphic product is to communicate information. Often **designers** have to communicate complex information with limited space and without fear of being misunderstood. Designers of graphic products must develop skills to communicate visually. Being able to make information and instructions easy to follow, and to create designs that make an impact, are the basis of good design.

Making an impact

Graphic designs that grab your attention by using designs, words or symbols to get a message across are often called 'impact graphics'. Impact graphics use visual persuasion to get people to buy a product or to warn, instruct or inform.

One of the main ways of grabbing attention is to choose a bold colour such as red. Red is a very aggressive colour. It stands out from the shelf and when used with a contrasting colour such as white, it has a very positive impact.

Using symbols

To make communication easier and more direct designers use a range of symbols. A symbol stands for something. It is a simple graphic that represents an object, process or instruction. Look carefully at the signs and symbols on this page and you will see that they all SCORE. The word score helps you to remember the important characteristics of a symbol. All symbols should be:

Simple
Clear and have an
Obvious meaning that
Relates to an object, process or instruction and are
Easy to remember.

Symbols are designed using simple geometric shapes such as the square, triangle, circle, diamond and combinations of these.

Using colour

Colour is often used to improve the performance of a symbol. Red is used to indicate danger or stop, whilst green is used to represent go. In the United Kingdom, the British Standards Institute produces guidelines and recommendations on all types of signs and symbols. For safety signs specific colours are used. Red is used to prohibit, black and yellow for danger (especially on dangerous machinery), green for safety.

A range of graphic products using symbols and impact graphics

Pictograms

One of the simplest and most effective uses of the symbol is a **pictogram**. Pictograms are symbols often used to represent activities or events that involve people. Like all symbols, pictograms are stylized images that tell you something quickly. The word stylized means taking a quite complex image and creating a much simpler more straightforward image that keeps the essential features of the original.

A stylized image of athlete keeps the essential characteristics of the image, but is much simpler

Breaking the language barrier

Pictograms do not rely upon language. Wherever you go in the world, pictograms are used to communicate information because they are used without writing.

Pictograms used on this sign do not rely on an understanding of language

Signs

When a symbol is used on its own or with other symbols to direct and instruct, it becomes a sign. All of us are used to reading the shorthand of signs. Most people are so familiar with road signs, for example, that they read them, understand them and act upon them without really thinking. These signs, however, are the result of careful design.

Some common road signs

Communicating a process

Symbols are also widely used to explain processes. They help to make a process easier to understand. Look at the process shown on the side of a packet of washing powder. Try and work out what the process is.

DOSAGE INSTRUCTIONS FOR AUTOMATIC MACHINES			
Soft Water	2	2	3
Medium Water	2	2	3
Hard Water	2	2	3
Handwashing or Soaking : These tablets are not recommended for these functions.			

Washing instructions

Activity

1 Explain using notes and **sketches** what is meant by the term stylisation.

Key point

● Symbols must conform to the 'SCORE' test – they must be Simple, Clear, Obvious, Relate to an object or activity and be Easy to remember.

Bringing drawings to life

The impact of colour

Colour is an essential ingredient in the success of all graphic products. Colour communicates meaning and it defines moods. Colour is also an important element in the **aesthetics** (appeal) of a product.

Aesthetics

The word aesthetics comes from the Greek word *aesthete*, which means beautiful. So aesthetics is about how products are made appealing or beautiful to people. This can be through taste, touch, smell, sound, or any of the senses, although it is usually about the visual appearance of a product.

To say that a product is aesthetically pleasing usually means that things like the size, colour, shape and form look right to a person. All these elements contribute to the aesthetics of a product, but to a graphic **designer**, colour and how it is used is a very important factor.

Colour theory

Colour affects the way we feel about a particular product. Have you ever wondered why some things go together whilst others clash? Deciding on the most suitable colours for a design is more complex than simply picking a favourite colour.

Primary, secondary and tertiary colours

In design work, the **primary colours** are red, yellow and blue. They are called primary (first) because they cannot be made from other colours and from these colours (with white and black **tone**), all the other colours can be made.

The primary colours

The secondary colours

By mixing the primary colours, the **secondary colours** – orange, purple and green – are produced:

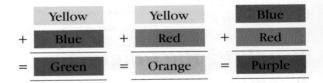

Yellow		Yellow		Blue
+ Blue		+ Red		+ Red
= Green		= Orange		= Purple

By mixing a primary colour with a secondary colour, a third colour called a tertiary colour is produced. The colour wheel below shows how each colour is formed.

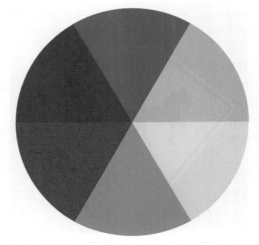

A colour wheel

Using colour in design

Complementary colours

Have you ever noticed that some colours work well together and some don't? Colours that are opposite each other on the colour wheel create contrast and improve the appearance of each other. They are called **complementary colours**.

Complementary colours

Orange complements blue.
Red complements green.
Yellow complements purple.

Harmonizing colours

Colours that are neighbours on the colour wheel – like yellow and orange – are called harmonizing colours. This means that they look pleasing, or are in harmony with one another.

yellow ⟶ orange

Yellow and orange are neighbours on the colour wheel – they harmonize with one another

Harmonizing colours such as yellow and green are so close together on the colour wheel that they do not create any contrast. Therefore, they should not be used on products such as **logos** that might need to be photocopied. When photocopied, the colours blend together and the image loses its quality and definition.

Blending colours with a pencil

Colours that harmonize such as orange and red can be blended together with a pencil to give pleasing graphic effects. This can only be achieved with neighbours on the colour wheel.

Red and yellow are harmonizing colours – they can be blended together well

Hue and tone

The actual colour such as blue or red, is called the **hue**. The hue can be changed by adding **tone**. The tone is the amount of light or dark (black or white) that is used.

100%–0% tone

The effect of adding tone to hue

Colour associations

Colour also affects the way we feel about things because we create associations with different colours in our own minds. Red is often associated with danger; yellow and black stripes (such as those on a wasp) are a warning. Blue is cold; orange is warm. Colour associations are used cleverly by designers to communicate meaning. Cleansing products such as toothpaste are most commonly white and blue. How would you feel about using brown toothpaste?

Activity

1 Using the packaging, explain how colour has been used by the designer to communicate information about a product.

Key points

- Aesthetics is the art of making things beautiful – it involves all our senses, but in graphic products it is most concerned with the appearance of a product.

Using colour

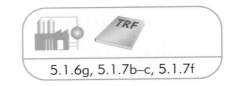
Why colour?

Colour is used to bring a drawing to life. It can make a particular part of a drawing stand out, make it look more attractive, or help communicate details about the object such as the material it is made from.

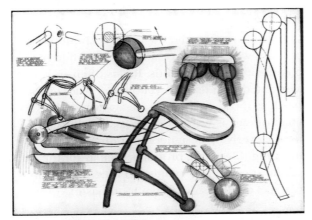

Colour helps to bring sketches to life

Making a form out of a shape

Colour is often added to a drawing to show its form. The form of an object is what it looks like in 3D, as opposed to shape, which is what an object looks like in 2D. Compare the two drawings of a torch below. The colour shows the contours and raised areas on the torch. Often colour is the main clue you have about an object's form.

A flat and a rendered torch

Different materials, different techniques

As **designers**, we often need to convey detail about the material an object is made from. When colour is evenly applied to an object, it does not gives us any clues about this.

Flat colour does not provide any clues about the material the object is made from

In order to give an impression of the material used, designers use a number of different graphic effects. If the material is non-reflective, like wood, a base colour similar to that of the wood is applied first. The grain is then added using a pencil or pen.

Using pencils or pens to imitate the material creates interest and helps to communicate information about the product

Reflections or surface detail can be seen in most plastics, metals or painted surfaces. Very shiny materials such as chrome or mirrored glass actually reflect pictures or objects close to them. One technique for showing that a material is reflective, such as mirror or chrome, is to use very dark contrasting lines or shapes.

The reflective surface of chrome can be represented using bold contrast

Making it shine

Materials that are shiny such as glass or **acrylic** are usually represented by using a number of short parallel lines drawn diagonally across a surface as shown below.

The reflective line technique

The rules for shiny surfaces

● On horizontal surfaces, such as a table top, the parallel lines are drawn vertically.

● On vertical surfaces, such as a window pane, the parallel lines are drawn at approximately 45 degrees.

● Where an object is coloured, such as red acrylic, the shiny surface can be shown by removing parallel lines with an eraser to show the white surface underneath.

Rounded edges

When light falls on a rounded surface such as a cylinder or a cone, different amounts of light will be reflected. The part of the surface immediately facing the light source will reflect the most light. This is represented by a white stripe on the rendered object. As the surface curves away from the light, less light is reflected and hence it appears darker.

Light reflected off a pyramid, cone and cylinder

Activity

1 Explain, using two examples, how colour can be used to show the form of an object.

Key points

● Colour can be used effectively to show the form (3D shape) of an object.

● There are different techniques for showing the type of material used.

Adding texture and tone

Textures

The surface of a material can be shiny, rough, matt, smooth, hard or soft. All of these words describe the feel or texture of a surface. We are able to see texture (as well as feel it) because of the way that light falls on to the surface. With a course texture such as concrete, the surface is made up of a series of lumps and hollows. The raised lumps cast a shadow and the hollows absorb the light and appear darker.

Many of the materials that are used within graphic products have textured surfaces. By studying the way that the light falls on to them we can use a range of techniques to represent the shadows, patterns and reflections seen.

The blocks of texture on the left show a representative sample of different graphic techniques used for different textures. Many of these textures have been created using a computer.

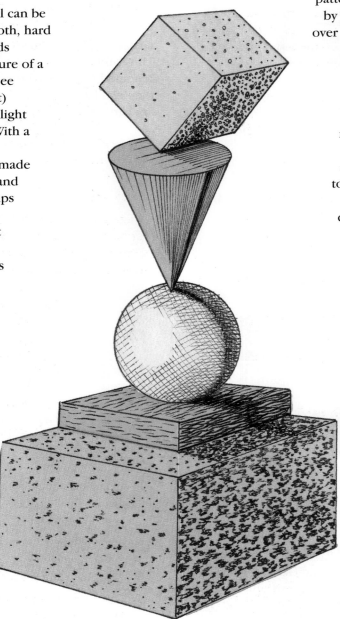

Lines and dots represent the surface of the materials

However, some of the patterns have been achieved by placing a piece of paper over the surface and rubbing lightly with a pencil. The drawings below use lines and dots to represent the surface of the materials. You will notice that the texturing has not been evenly applied. This is not only to show the effect of light and shade but also to create more interest and make the object appear more realistic.

The importance of texture

It is important to show texture in **design** drawings because it leads to a more effective presentation. Drawings produced with added texture are more interesting visually and more importantly, they communicate information about the material used clearly.

Light and shade

When we produce a pictorial drawing of an object the outline defines the flat shape. In reality, you never see the outlines of an object, you simply see different areas of light and shade.

One effective way of making a drawing more realistic is to apply shading to it. When light falls on an object it reflects back a certain amount of light. The different surfaces of the object reflect different amounts of light – the more light they reflect, the lighter they seem.

The effect of light on different surfaces

When you apply light and shade to an object the simple rules to follow are:

- horizontal surfaces reflect more light than vertical surfaces
- the surfaces nearest the light source reflect more light.

Using a pencil to shade

A soft pencil such as a 2B is ideal for producing a range of **tones**. By applying differing amounts of pressure on the pencil, tonal shading is produced. It is called tonal shading because one colour is used and the form of an object is shown through the tonal differences.

Tonal range card made by shading with a 2B pencil

Using coloured paper

A very effective graphic technique used by designers for showing light and shade is to use white pencil shading. If a dark paper such as black or grey is used, a negative image is produced. When using this method you have to work in reverse, but otherwise the toning is the same as with a normal pencil. Highlights are emphasised with solid white.

White pencil shading is an effective graphic technique

Line shading

An alternative and much quicker way of shading an object is to use lines. By varying the number of lines, their thickness and their spacing, shading can be achieved.

Line shading is a quick way to shade an object

Activity

1 The difference between light and dark tones is called the contrast. Explain why contrast is an important feature of graphic illustrations.

Key points

- Adding textures to a drawing makes it more interesting and realistic. Textures can be represented with patterns of lines and dots.
- Contrast helps to define the form of the object.

Mechanisms and pop-ups

Creating pop-ups is an exciting way of producing graphic products. Pop-ups use paper engineering techniques to help bring stories to life and create impact and appeal. Some of the most interesting examples of pop-ups can be found in children's books where they help to create the interest needed to stimulate learning. There are some good examples in the picture on the right.

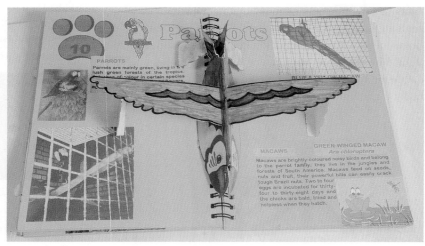

Pages from a pop-up book

The basics of making things move

When designing pop-ups, there are certain conventions for the types of folds used. There are three main types of fold:

● Valley folds – marked 1 on the drawing below. With valley folds, the crease goes away from you as the page is folded.

● Mountain folds – marked 2 on the drawing opposite. With mountain folds, the crease goes towards you as the page is folded.

● The spine – marked 3 on the drawing below. This is the fold down the centre of the page.

Folding techniques

The simple V fold

The V fold is one of the most widely used mechanisms for producing movement in a page. By adding graphics to the pop-up, exciting **designs** can be created.

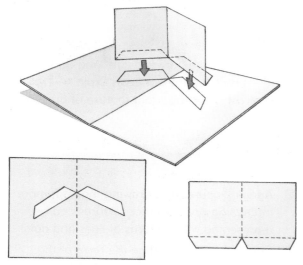

Valley, mountain and spine folds

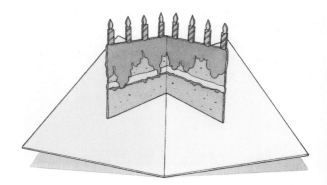

Making a V fold

1 Make sure that the two angles marked A are exactly the same. This is important. They should be less than 90 degrees, but no more than 60 degrees.

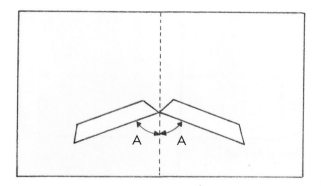

2 Carefully score along the line B (scoring means using a pen to compress the fibres of the paper). Make sure that the vertical crease is exactly 90 degrees.

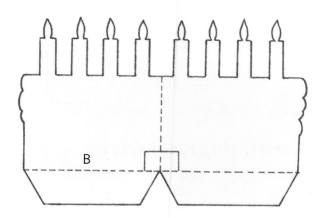

3 As the card is folded, the pop-up folds down and backwards away from you. When making a V fold, make sure that it is positioned near the front of the card, otherwise it will stick out at the top when the card is closed.

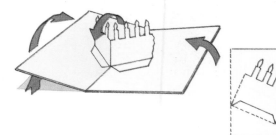

Fold variations

Multiple V folds

Exciting pop-ups can be made by combining simple V folds. These are more challenging, but enable you to develop a 3D view. When making multiple V folds, make sure that all the creases are exactly in line, otherwise the pop-up will not close properly.

V folds pointing forwards

These add interest to pop-ups and allow space on the page for text such as a story to be added. The rules for forward pointing V folds are the same as for the backward version and different effects can be created by using different angles.

Activity

1 Using a V fold, design a simple greetings card for a friend.

Key points

● There are three types of basic fold.
● Successful V folds require very accurate measurements and cutting.

Pop-ups – the parallelogram

The parallelogram

The second basic building block for making successful pop-ups is the parallelogram. Parallelograms provide a solid 3D form when the card is fully open.

As with pop-up constructions, when making a pop-up based upon the parallelogram, it is essential that all measurements and angles are accurately drawn.

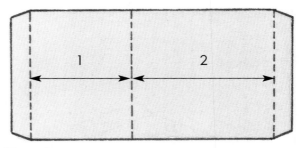

View of pop-up

Parallelogram

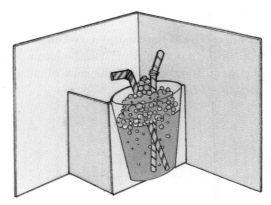

Glass of fizzy drink set on a parallelogram

Making a parallelogram

Make sure that the two sticking areas are exactly parallel to the spine and that the lengths 1 and 2 on the base are the same as the pop-up piece.

Care must be taken to ensure that the pop-up does not stick out when the card is closed. This will be avoided by making measurement 3 longer than 2 and 4 longer than 1.

Parallelogram ideas

More complex and exciting pop-ups can be created by building different layers of parallelograms. The largest shapes are placed at the back and the smallest at the front. In this way, complex scenes can be built up.

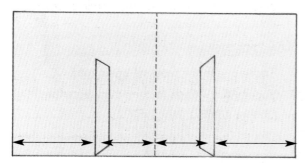

Base piece

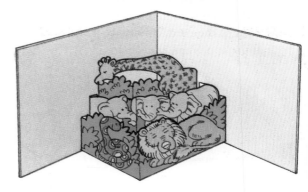

Simple parallelograms built up in layers

Adding muscle

Another useful way of using the parallelogram pop-up is to use it as a lever or 'muscle' in order to raise a much larger image. This type of arrangement is commonly used on simple pop-up greetings cards.

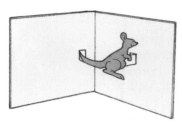

A small parallelogram is often used to lift a much larger image

Parallelograms without glue

The parallelogram can be cut from the base

It is not always essential to build pop-ups from separate pieces of card. If you are really accurate, you can cut out the shape from the base.

With this type of pop-up, all the scored lines must be parallel to the spine (see page 77). These can be either horizontal or vertical.

Cutting a parallelogram from the base

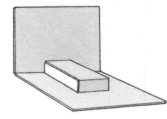 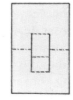

Base and fold up cut parallelogram

Look carefully at the drawing below. Decide upon the length and depth of the parallelogram, then:

1 Draw the spine carefully with a pencil.

2 Above the spine, draw and score line 1.

3 Below the spine, draw and then score line 2.

4 Mark out and cut lies 3 and 4 (length and depth of the parallelogram).

5 Mark out and score the crease (line 3) that is equal to the length of the parallelogram.

6 Score the two parts of the spine that are outside the cuts.

7 Push out the parallelogram. You will notice that the crease becomes a mountain fold whilst lines 1 and 2 are valley folds.

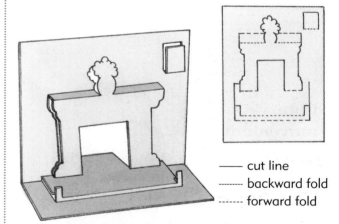

——— cut line
------- backward fold
------- forward fold

Once you become confident in using cut parallelogram techniques, a wide variety of designs can be produced

Activiy

1 Design and produce a cut parallelogram with a picture of a person of your choice glued on to the front face.

Key point

● All measurements and angles on parallelogram pop-ups must be accurately measured.

Moving with mechanisms

A mechanism is defined as any system that creates or changes movement of an object. The four main types of movement are: linear, rotary, reciprocating and oscillating.

Linear movement

Linear means in a straight line. This type of movement occurs when a drawer is pulled open.

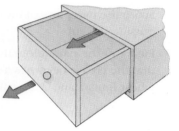

Linear movement

Rotary movement

Rotary or circular movement occurs when an object is rotated, such as a car wheel turning.

Rotary movement

Reciprocating movement

Reciprocating, or backwards and forwards movement, occurs within a car engine where the piston goes up and down continuously.

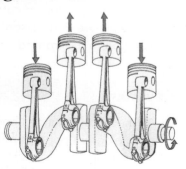

Reciprocating movement

Oscillating movement

Oscillating or rocking movement occurs when an object swings from side to side, such as a clock pendulum.

Oscillating movement

Changing the direction of movement

One of the most useful types of mechanism is one that changes one type of movement into another. For example, when a key is turned in a lock, the rotary movement of the key is turned into the linear movement of the bolt. The main movement types can be achieved using simple paper engineering mechanisms and combined with pop-up techniques to create dynamic graphics products.

Changing movement with paper mechanisms

Linear to rotary

This type of mechanism is produced using simple sliding arms (strips of paper or card that operate the mechanism). Linear to rotary mechanisms produce 'rocking' characters on cards and pop-ups. The most efficient sliding arms use a combination of slit and sleeve. Different **designs** can now be use added to the sliding arms to create interesting pop-ups.

Arm waving on fixed pivot.

Making things rock
Reciprocating to oscillating

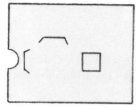 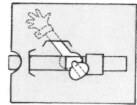

The most efficient sliding arms use a combination of slit and sleeve.

This mechanism converts reciprocating movement to oscillating and can form the basis of exciting designs. The basic components of the mechanism are shown on the right. Part A on the main wheel goes through slot B on the sliding arm. The flaps on the wheel (labelled C) go

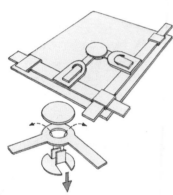

through hole D in the base and then fold flat. The rocking character is glued on to these flaps. Notice that there is a sleeve and a slot on the base to hold and support the sliding arm.

Front and back view of a rocking card

Turning movement through 90 degrees

Creating a mechanism that changes the direction of movement through 90 degrees is very useful when designing pop-ups. The mechanisms uses a linkage (usually a straight strip of card that connects the image to the sliding arm).

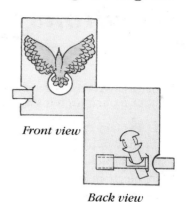

Front view

Back view

As the sliding arm is pulled, the image moves vertically (at 90 degrees to the sliding arm). When using this mechanism, it is very important to cut the slits accurately to control the direction of the movement.

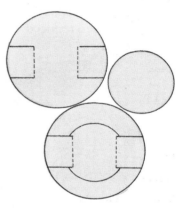

The connector holds the pieces of card together whilst allowing them to rotate

The main components needed to produce a rocking pop-up

Activity

1 Design a paper mechanism that combines a series of sliding arms to represent children playing hide and seek.

Key point

● The four main types of motion can be created using paper engineering techniques.

Questions

1 Pictorial sketches of a design for a page in a children's pop-up book are shown below.

   a Explain the function of the design feature shown in enlarged detail below.

   b Complete the side view of the card mechanism by adding an arrow to show the direction of corner X when the tab moves in the direction shown.

   c Add to the side view, the position of the mechanism when the vertical height of face B has been reduced to 20 mm by pushing the tab.

2 Using a range of **sketches** with notes, design a pop-up picture to go with the following text taken from a children's book.

'The driver of the bus rocked from side to side as the big wheels turned.'

The picture must:

- use a suitable mechanism
- be bright and eye-catching
- clearly show the story.

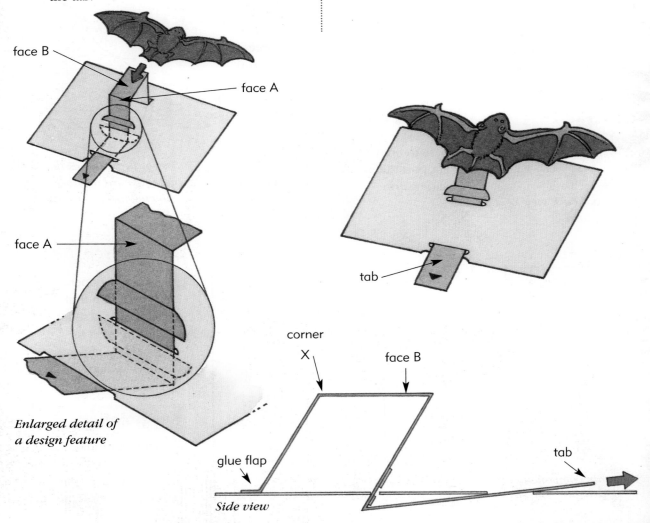

face B

face A

Enlarged detail of a design feature

face A

corner X

face B

glue flap

Side view

tab

tab

REALIZING DESIGN

Designed by BOB FLETCHER

Nets (developments)

The product unfolds

A **net**, or **development** as it is often called, is the flat shape of a package or display stand that has been unfolded. Nets can be complicated to **design**, especially if they are unusual shapes. A good way of understanding the principle of net design is to look at a simple die.

3D view of a die

When designing a net, it is very important that all the faces of the product are in the correct position. Working out the faces of a die net is a useful starting point.

The net of a die

Cut and fold lines

When nets are designed, the fold lines (which are always shown as dotted) are scored so that they bend easily. To score a line, a blunt knife or ball point pen is pressed on to the line, deforming the surface of the card or thin plastic. Scoring the line helps the net to fold easily. The outlines (solid lines) are pre-cut, and the net is ready for folding.

A net usually has tabs added so that when folded it can be easily joined. The tabs overlap the edges where they meet and are glued in place. Sometimes packages lock together without glue. This is done to reduce the cost of packaging and increase the speed of production.

Looking at the product

Often designers want to cut a window or opening into the package so that the customer can see the product. The window is covered with a small sheet of clear plastic. A good example of this is Easter egg packaging.

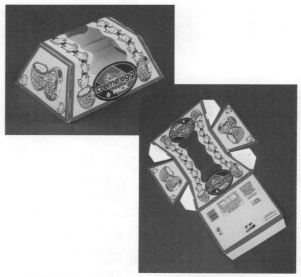

Packaging for products such as Easter eggs have clear plastic windows cut into the net so that customers can see the product

Developments

Nets of more complicated shapes such as cones have traditionally been called 'developments' because the flat shape is developed using simple geometry.

Curved surfaces

Drawing developments of objects that have curved surfaces such as the cylinder or cone require the use of geometry. The first stage in producing the development of a cylinder is to draw an accurate front **elevation** and plan.

The width of the development can be developed by dividing the plan into 12 equal segments. Now, draw a vertical line equal to the height of the cylinder. Using a pair of dividers or compasses, step off 12 divisions and you will produce a rectangle, which is the true shape of the cylinder. (Alternatively the width of the development can be calculated mathematically.)

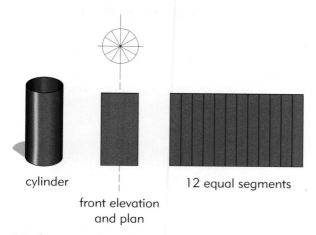

cylinder

front elevation and plan

12 equal segments

Development of a cylinder

The development of a cone

The development of a cone is actually a sector (part) of a circle. As for the cylinder above, the starting point for the development of a cone is an accurate front elevation and plan – this is important because the true height (slant height) of the cone is needed.

Draw a vertical line equal to the slant height of the cone. From the top of this line, draw an arc equal to the slant height. Now simply set the compasses to the width of the 30-degree sector on the plan and step it off 12 times on the development.

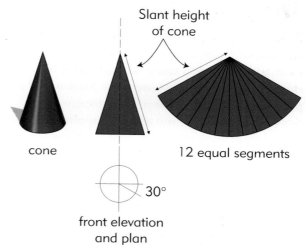

Slant height of cone

cone

12 equal segments

30°

front elevation and plan

Development of a cone

Activities

1 Draw the development for a carton that must hold 10 floppy disks. The carton must have glue tabs and it must have a lid.

2 Draw the development of a cone. The cone has a base diameter of 100 mm and is 150 mm high.

Key points

- Nets are the true shape of an object that has been folded out flat.

- More complicated nets such as a cone or cylinder need to be 'developed' using simple geometry.

- Nets must always show cut lines (solid lines) and fold lines (dotted).

Point of sale displays

AIDA

It has been said that for any graphic product to be successful it must **Attract**, create **Interest**, stimulate **Desire** and cause **Action** – AIDA for short. One way that **designers** use AIDA to sell a product is through **point of sale** displays.

Next time you go into a bank, supermarket or record shop, look at the way that products are introduced to the customer. Specially designed displays made from card are often used. These displays are produced cheaply because they only need to last for the length of the product promotion. Point of sale displays sometimes hold leaflets, using bright bold colours to attract attention and encourage shoppers to take one.

At the cash desk

The term point of sale display means the place at which goods are sold. Everyone who buys something in a shop must pay at the cash desk. It is here that point of sale displays are often found. People often have to wait to be served. While they are waiting they are a captive audience. A point of sale display on the counter gives people something to read and, hopefully, to buy.

A point of sale display

Hiring a video

If you ever have a problem thinking of what video to hire, just go into a video shop and you will be hit by lots of different point of sale displays giving you ideas.

When a new video is launched, special displays are produced. Point of sale displays for new videos are often large cardboard cut-outs of characters from the film. They are designed to attract customers and are always placed in prominent positions.

A point of sale display promoting a video

A successful display

A point of sale display might simply be a special arrangement of the products themselves placed in a special case. More usually, point of sale displays are part of a product promotion and involve posters, stickers and signs.

To be successful, point of sale displays must attract customers. Where they are placed can be as important as their design. In order to achieve maximum exposure to customers, point of sale displays are often fully 3D so that they can be seen from all sides.

Attracting attention

One way that point of sale displays attract attention is to use slogans. Slogans are headlines that are short, snappy and make you look twice. Often the slogan holds some form of intrigue or clue to make the customer think. Look carefully · at the point of sale display below to see how the designer has used a slogan to attract attention.

The slogan makes this point of sale display very effective

Key features of a point of sale display

When designing and making a point of sale display, you must make sure that it:

- is interesting and eye-catching

- is cheap to produce because it has a short life and is then thrown away

- is strong because it may be pushed and knocked

- can be flat packed because it will probably be posted to shops that will use it

- clearly links to the product so that the customer is left in no doubt what is being promoted

- is simple to print to keep the cost down.

Often these displays involve complex **nets**, folds and cut-outs. It is important that when the display is folded into its correct shape, all the printing is in the right place. To keep the cost of production down, point of sale displays should be printed on one side only.

Twisting and turning

To achieve one-sided printing, a display often has a special turning joint which allows it to be turned before folding.

The bottom half is printed upside down so that it is in the correct position when it is twisted and folded into place

Activity

1 Write a six point **specification** for a point of sale display designed to promote a new children's film.

Key points

- Point of sale displays need to conform to the AIDA rule – they must Attract the customer, be Interesting, create Desire and lead to Action.

- They are made from card and thin plastic. This is because they must be cheap to produce because they are only used for a short time.

- They can be highly complex and are often made from more than one piece of card. In order for all the printing to be on one side, they often incorporate a turning.

Unwrapping the packing

Made to be thrown away

Packaging is the ultimate example of ephemera – things that are designed to be short lived. Ephemeral products such as packaging, bus and cinema tickets, promotional flyers and posters are made, used, then thrown away. Indeed, it is said that over 80% of all household rubbish comes from packaging – what a waste!

Most household rubbish comes from packaging

The functions of packaging

The **function** of a product is what it does – its purpose. Packaging has three distinct functions: to sell the product, to protect the product's contents and to communicate information to the customers.

Selling the product

For packaging, as with most areas of graphic products, the impact of the **design** is very important. People often make decisions based upon first impressions. The ability of a piece of packaging to attract, create interest and desire are essential to success. Some of the most successful brands in the world use a bright red background. Red is an aggressive selling colour; it stands out from the shelf and creates impact.

Gold is seen as a mark of quality. Athletes are often awarded a gold medal when they win a race as proof that they are the best. The same psychology is used to sell products.

Creating demand – the 'strawberry effect'

One of the reasons that people like strawberries so much is that they are only available for a short time every year. Because we can't have strawberries whenever we want them, the demand for them during the summer is huge. When marketing products, the 'strawberry effect' is used to create demand. A good example of this is the Cadbury's 'creme' egg. Only marketed during the run up to Easter (from January), the **advertising** focuses upon the short time that they are available – get yours now while you have the chance.

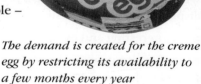

The demand is created for the creme egg by restricting its availability to a few months every year

Protecting the product

Probably the most important function of packaging is to protect the product from breaking or perishing. What good would a tin of soup be without a container? How many eggs would break in the shopping basket if they were not held securely in a box?

The clever design of the egg box provides excellent protection for its fragile contents

Food must be protected by law. Most foods need to be vacuum sealed to prevent them from perishing by exposure to air. The packaging has to be there, so why not use it to sell the product?

Blister packaging

Blister packaging is used to keep the contents from falling out. Blister packages are made from one piece of card with a clear plastic bubble **vacuum formed** over the product.

Blister packaging contains the product and provides a window so that the product can be seen by the customer

An important feature of blister packing is that the product can be seen clearly. This is an important selling feature. By using a rigid thermoplastic such as Polyvinyl Chloride (PVC) as the blister material, the packaging also provides excellent protection.

Communicating information

Packaging communicates two very different types of information – the overt (open information) and the covert (closed or hidden messages).

The overt

By law, packaging must display certain information, such as the type of product, its weight and details about the company that produced it. It will often give the buyer instructions on how to use the product. In the case of food, these instructions will usually be about cooking and freezing. There is also a barcode which gives coded information to the shopkeeper. Information like this is often put on the back of the packaging because it does not help to sell the product.

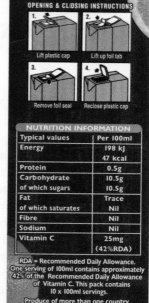

Instructions on the back or sides of packaging provide information, but do not sell the product

The covert

Covert or closed information uses images and text to persuade customers to buy the product. Cat food tins always show pictures of well-fed, happy looking cats and chocolate wrappers do not tell you that the product is full of sugar. How many times do you open a ready meal only to find that the actual product is a lot smaller than it looks on the picture?

The design of the packaging also helps to target the product at the right market. Compare the differences between a packet of chocolate buttons and a jar of hair gel. Look carefully at the colours, pictures and images. It is through these that the designer communicates all the unwritten information that customers use to make their decision to buy.

Activity

1 Name the three functions of packaging.

Key points

- Packaging is an example of an ephemeral (short-lived) product– once it has been used it is thrown away

Materials in action 1

Choosing the right material

When you write a **design specification** for a new graphic product, one of the key considerations will be the choice of material. Each material has its own distinct properties. Some materials are hard, some soft, some are rigid or flexible. For example, an estate agent's sign needs to be rigid and water resistant. At the development stage of the design process, you will need to carry out **research** into the materials that will give you the performance you require.

Deciding on the property

The property of a material is different from its characteristics. Usually, properties are considered to be things that are **quantitative**. Properties are therefore things that can be measured. Common material properties that are considered for graphic products are:

- weight
- stiffness/rigidity/flexibility
- density
- ease of printing
- strength
- water resistance.

   The characteristics of a material are such things as its texture, or feel and its appearance. However, with materials used for graphic products both the characteristics and properties can be changed through printing and forming.

Paper and board

Papers come in a variety of weights, colours and textures. The choice of paper is important and can greatly affect the quality of the final product. Paper is weighed in grams per square metre (**gsm**).

This is a standardized system for grading paper and it means the weight of a piece of paper that is 1 metre square. The higher the number, the greater the density (thickness) of the paper. For example, most paper used for photocopying is 90 gsm. This, in paper terms, is quite a low cost, lightweight paper.

Paper sizes

The most common range of paper sizes is the 'A' range. You will be most familiar with A4 paper. Each time the paper is halved in size, its value goes up by one. So A4 is half the size of A3, A3 is half the size of A2, and so on.

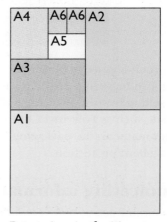

Paper sizes in the 'A' range

Boards

Boards are heavy paper. Usually, papers become boards when their weight is more than 200 gsm. Boards are treated to give them different properties and characteristics. Often board is produced as a duplex, which means two different types of board joined together. Duplex board is found on boxes and cartons where one surface is bleached white for printing and the other is left as pure wood pulp. Boards can be strengthened with a corrugated layer on the inside. They are often coated with a metallized foil to make them waterproof, as on drinks cartons.

Material	Advantages	Used for
Newsprint	Lightweight, accepts all types of ink	Newspapers
Cartridge paper	Good quality, provides a good surface for pencil, pens, markers. The name comes from the original use for the paper which formed the tube section of a shotgun shell	Design drawings, sketch pads
Sugar paper	Has contrasting colours which are useful for tonal drawings	Mounting work, displays
Cardboard	Cheap, rigid, good printing surface, recyclable	Packaging, cartons and boxes
Corrugated card	Very strong, lightweight, recyclable	Packaging fragile products
White board	Bleached surface, very strong, excellent for printing	Book covers, quality packaging
Duplex board	Cheaper than solid white board, provides an alternative textured surface for printing	Food packaging
Cast coated boards (similar to bleached white card, though cast coating achieves a heavier and smoother surface)	High quality products that require a high gloss finish	Provides an excellent surface for printing, varnishing and embossing
Foil-lined board (laminated on to the surface of a variety of boards to provide a waterproof liner)	Drinks or cosmetics cartons	Provides a moisture proof barrier – can be matt or gloss

Different types of paper used for graphic products

Common paper terms

- Coating – a layer of minerals applied to one or both sides of paper or board to improve brightness, gloss and printability. The mineral most often used is china clay.

- Filler – a material such as china clay or calcium carbonate that is added to make a paper smoother or increase opacity.

- Laminate – used as an overlay on sheets of paper or board, either with other materials such as plastic, or metal foil to form a product with special qualities.

- Opacity – the property of a material that prevents light being seen through it.

- Ream – a unit of measurement for sheets of paper, usually 500.

Activity

1 Explain what is meant by the term 200 gsm duplex board.

Key points

- The quality of a paper or board is defined by factors such as its weight (in grams) and its surface treatment.

- Special treatments are applied to paper and board to give them distinct properties. The higher the quality, the more expensive they are.

Materials in action 2

Plastics ·

Plastics are widely used in packaging because they are cheap, tough, easily printed on to and are usually flexible enough to be used for squeezing. This makes them perfect for containers such as bottles and tubes. Plastics can be made clear or opaque and can be made, with the addition of pigments (colours), into a wide variety of colours. Also, plastic can be manufactured in a range of complex shapes and can have virtually any surface texture applied. This makes plastic ideal for graphic products, particularly liquid containers, because of its strength and waterproof properties.

Bottles and containers

A variety of blow-moulded plastic containers

Commercially, bottles and hollow containers are usually made by the process of blow-moulding. With blow moulding, a thin tube of plastic is first heated and softened to make it easy to mould. It is then gripped between the two halves of a bottle-shaped mould and air is blown into the mould under pressure. The pressure of the air causes the plastic to take the shape of the mould. The mould is rapidly cooled and the container is formed.

Laminated plastics

One of the most common forms of plastics used for the manufacture of graphic products is 'corriflute'. Corriflute is very similar to corrugated cardboard. It is made from three layers of thin plastic, with the centre layer fluted to provide extra strength. It has the advantage of a very high strength-to-weight ratio and is particularly useful for producing signs and 3D **prototype** models. It is widely used for signs and products such as **portfolio** cases because of its stiffness and light weight.

Corriflute is a versatile modelling material because it is lightweight yet strong and stiff

Foamboard

Foamboard is a special **laminate** of paper and plastic. The outer layers are usually bleached cardboard sandwiching a layer of very lightweight polystyrene foam. It is particularly useful for graphic product modelling because it is a strong, lightweight material that can easily be cut. The card surface can easily be **rendered** or printed on. It also has the advantage of being able to be joined using PVA wood glue.

Modern materials such as carbon fibre are changing the way products are designed and made

Modern materials

Rapid developments in technology mean that new materials are being continuously produced. Many of these materials can be combined to form composites that have remarkable properties. A composite material is one made from two or more materials.

A good example of a modern material is carbon fibre. Carbon fibre is a composite made from carbon fibres bonded with a flexible plastic resin. It is very lightweight, yet incredibly strong. Such is the strength of this new material that it is used to form the cab of Formula 1 racing cars and can absorb the forces of 200 mph collisions.

Smart materials

Many modern materials are now termed 'smart' because they are able to respond to changes. In the commercial manufacturing of graphic products, many smart materials are now being used in a variety of products. A good example of a smart graphic material is photochromic ink.

Photochromic inks change their colour depending upon the temperature. For example, when used in a product such as a pen, the hand holding the pen warms the ink and it changes colour. Although this is a novelty example, photochromic ink is also used on temperature gauges to give a quick visual signal of temperature change.

When used with cotton or other textiles, garments such as shirts and trousers can be made that change colour according to temperature. Photochromic inks can have a medical use when used with surgical cloths because they indicate a rise in temperature, a common sign of infection.

Modern materials in manufacturing

They are many new materials used in graphic product manufacture that make products more useful or efficient. Many adhesives such as double-sided tapes and special glues that react to ultra-violet light or heat are now in common use as strong and quick-setting adhesives.

A useful source of further information on new and smart materials is the Internet. The Internet search engine www.google.com lists thousands of examples of new materials. Simply go to the site and enter 'smart materials' and you will be spoilt for choice!

Activity

1 Why are smart materials called this?

Key points

- A composite material is a new material made from a mixture of two or more materials.
- Many modern materials are composites.
- Composite materials often have unique properties.

Processes

Equipment and techniques

There are a wide variety of processes that you can use to produce your **designs**. Some use machines to help you form the designs and others use craft techniques.

Vacuum forming

This is a very cheap and useful way of producing simple forms in thin plastic sheet. It is used for producing blister packaging and shapes for containing and displaying products, such as screwdrivers.

Vacuum formed blister packaging

Making a vacuum form mould for an Easter egg

A material, usually wood, is carefully formed into the exact shape of half the egg. When making a mould it is important that there are clear angles on all sides so that the formed plastic will easily come off the mould when it has been formed.

Tiny holes are drilled around the base of the mould and over the surface of the mould, so that when the air is removed by the vacuum pump, the plastic film will wrap around it completely and no air will be trapped.

A wooden Easter egg

The process of vacuum forming

The vacuum forming machine consists of a heating element for heating the plastic, a platform that can be raised and lowered and a vacuum pump.

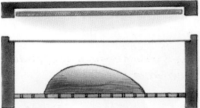

The mould is placed in the vacuum forming machine and a thin sheet of plastic is secured above it.

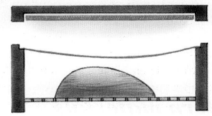

The plastic is heated until it becomes very floppy.

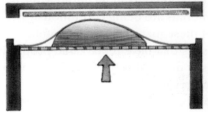

The vacuum pump is turned on. This sucks out all the air between the plastic and the mould.

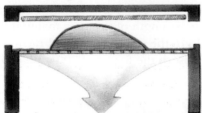

The plastic is sucked down over the mould. When the plastic is cool it sets into the shape of the mould.

Vacuum forming process

Laminating

Plastic **laminating** is a process used to protect graphic products from moisture. Laminating machines use heat and pressure to sandwich the work between two layers of plastic film.

Laminating is a very useful way of protecting products such as menus

Using a strip heater for line bending

A useful piece of equipment for bending straight lines and corners on thin plastic is the strip heater. Sometimes called the line bender it is particularly useful for making clear window inserts into packaging like that on the Jenga game. Strip heaters can only be used on thin sheet plastic such a high impact polystyrene and **acrylic**.

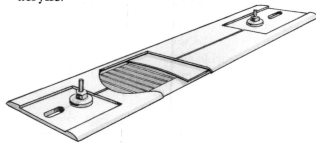

A strip heater

Special effects

One way of producing interesting backgrounds and effects on paper and card is to use the process of marbling. This process uses the principle that oil and water do not mix. A small amount of oil based paints are spread out on the surface of a water tank and then mixed with a stick. Dipping the paper or card into the tank will transfer the paint pattern onto the paper.

Example of a student's point of sale display with a marbled background

Often when we use plain manufactured woods that have no grain, like medium Density Fibre Board (**MDF**), it is difficult to get them to look attractive. Marbling can also be used for this although a background colour must first be used.

Activities

1 Name three common **thermoplastics**.
2 Give two advantages of the vacuum forming process.

Key points

- The processes used for making products out of thin plastic rely on the use of thermoplastics, such as acrylic and high impact polystyrene.
- Thermoplastics have plastic memory. This means that they can be reheated many times and they will always return to their original shape.

Models

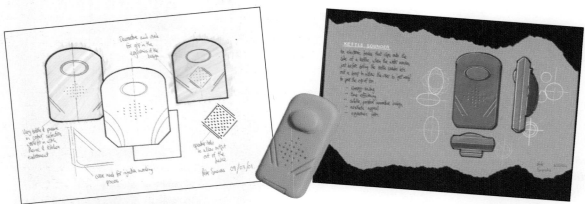

Concept modelling helps the designer to get a better understanding of what an idea looks and feels like

What is a model?

A model is something that is made to help the **designer** to test or **evaluate** an idea without having to make an actual product. A model can be a simple paper structure, a detailed **prototype** made from card, plastic or wood such as balsa and jelutong, or an image produced using computer software.

Why make a model?

The main **function** of a model is to help give the designer a better understanding of what the final product may look like. It is difficult to decide on whether a design is acceptable or not just by looking at a drawing. A full-scale model allows the designer to carry out tests and evaluations without having to go through the expense of making the real thing. Motor manufacturers make full-scale models in clay to evaluate the appearance and function of a new car design.

Concept modelling

Models are particularly useful to the designer during the design development stage. It is here that ideas or concepts can be quickly tested for shape, form and functional details.

The drawings above show a student's design ideas for a kettle sounder. Drawings like this are useful for looking at shape but the ideas can only be taken forward (developed) by getting a feel for what the product actually looks and feels like. This is achieved by making very basic concept models from styrofoam.

Testing the function

Sometimes when we are designing a product to work in a particular way, models can be used to simulate the mechanisms or movement needed. Test models do not necessarily have to look like the real thing as long as the working part of the model is realistic.

Paper model of a fold mechanism to be used in a folding map

Computer modelling

Computer models are a quick and inexpensive way of looking at the 3D form of a product. The image of a product can be created on a computer monitor and realistic colour and shading applied. Sophisticated computer programs allow this image to be rotated so that it can be seen from different angles. The image can be quickly changed and these changes modelled on screen, saving time and money.

Making changes

The main advantage of computer modelling is that changes can be made on screen. The pictures below show how the colour for a prototype telephone can be modelled on a computer.

The colour for a prototype telephone is modelled on computer

Modelling for evaluation

When carrying out an evaluation on a product it is useful to compare your design with similar products. Computer modelling can help by making a virtual catalogue.

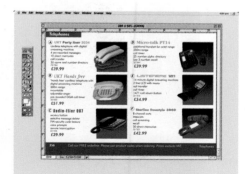

Firstly, a page from a catalogue is scanned into the computer

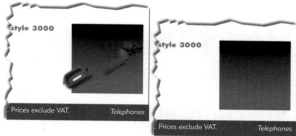

The image of a similar product is then 'rubbed out', leaving a blank background

The digital picture of the telephone can now be inserted on to the background

The final catalogue page. The telephone can now be evaluated against other similar products available

Activity

1 Explain why models are so important to the designer?

Key points

- Modelling is a means of quickly testing ideas and concepts.
- It is a very important part of design development because it allows the designer to answer the question 'What if?'.

Modelling

Modelling materials

The most common materials used for modelling in schools are foamcard, cardboard and thin plastic. Fillers, paints, plaster of paris and anything you can lay your hands on can be used as well.

Cardboard

Cardboard is probably the most widely used material for modelling. Cardboard can be made to look very realistic by the addition of surface papers. Brick and tile patterns can be printed off from the computer and added to make a model of a house look realistic.

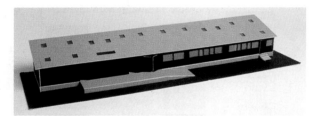

Brick and tile patterns make this model building look realistic

Thin plastic

Plastics such as **acrylic** and high impact polystyrene can be used to make representational models. Acrylic can be heat formed or used as a flat sheet. In the example opposite, a scale model of a shop window design has been made from acrylic.

Scale model of a shop window design made in acrylic

Expanded foam

Expanded foams such as polystyrene are used by **designers** as concept models. A concept model does not have any detail but it helps to give an impression of the shape, form and size of a product. Expanded foams are very crumbly and do not allow you to form any precise detail.

Foam crumbles very easily but it is useful as a concept model

Foamboard

Foamboard is made from three layers of material. The outer surfaces are made from good quality white cardboard, which sandwich a thin layer of foam. When foamboard is used with a **plotter cutter**, realistic models of **point of sale** displays can be made.

Using clay

Graphic designers use clay as a modelling material because it is easy to use. It takes great skill to produce a very detailed model, but clay can be useful for testing concepts such as **ergonomics**. Clay can also be used to make moulds for **vacuum forming** (see page 94).

Clay is a useful modelling material

Vacuum forming and plaster of paris

When making solid models one useful technique is to make a plastic mould of the product using the vacuum former. The plastic vacuum former can then be filled with plaster of paris. Once set, the plaster of paris model can easily be painted and other details applied.

Plaster of paris models of training shoes

Finishing models

The most effective models must always look realistic. A wide range of different effects can be achieved with a little thought and imagination.

Spirit markers

Graphic marker ink binds to the surface of shiny plastic and does not scrape off. This means it can be used as an alternative to spray paint for colouring plastic sheet.

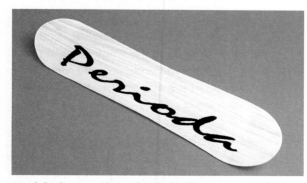

Model of a snowboard coloured using a graphic marker

Finishes on plastic

Stained glass paint

It is often quite difficult to give the impression of a printed effect on plastic. However, designs can be hand painted on to acrylic using special glass paints. These paints are water soluble and give a very realistic finish to the work.

Fashion models hand painted with stained glass paint

Activities

1   Explain the importance of modelling to the designer.

2   Give three different modelling materials used by design technologists and for each list their main advantages.

3   Using notes and **sketches**, describe the structure of foamboard.

Key points

- A wide range of modelling materials can be used to create a close likeness to your intended design.

- Materials such as plaster of paris are easy to paint and are useful for simulating products such as shoes and containers.

- Concept models do not have to show all the details of a final product because their purpose is to give an idea about the form and function of an idea.

Questions

1 Cardboard storage boxes are popular space-savers. The incomplete net/development for a box is shown below. Boxes are often sold as flat packs.

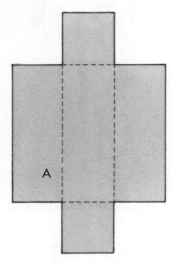

a State what the line labelled A represents.

b Add a lid to the net/development so that the box may be closed.

c Sketch a simple way of assembling the storage box without the need for using glue or tape.

2 The photo below shows a blister packaged bulb for a bedroom lamp.

a Name the process by which this blister packaging was formed. Using notes and sketches, describe this process in detail.

b State *three* different functions of packaging.

Many people are concerned about the environmental effects of the increased use of packaging.

c Explain how designers are becoming more environmentally friendly. Use two examples in your answer.

3 The picture below shows the front cover of a light for a child's room. It has been manufactured from rigid foamboard.

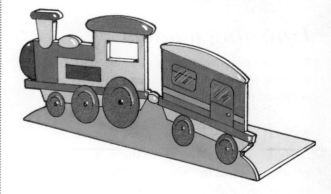

a Give *two* advantages of foamboard for use as a light cover.

b Name two alternative materials that could be used for making the front cover of the light. For each material, give one advantage to the manufacturer and one to the consumer.

GET THE MESSAGE

Marketing the product

What is marketing?

Marketing a product involves a complex relationship between the **designer**, the consumer and the product. At its simplest, this requires creating an image for a product or service which the consumer finds irresistible.

The functions of marketing

The three main **functions** of marketing are to:

- sell the product to customers
- communicate (information/messages)
- present/create an image that will persuade customers that they need the product or service advertised.

The marketing of design has given rise to a large industry in its own right and involves several groups of people. A food manufacturer who has developed a new product, or an insurance company that wants to introduce a new service, will contact a marketing agency to package and **advertise** it. A marketing team consisting of product development and business executives will then work with advertising, public relations and design consultancies to create an image or identity for the new product or service. Designers will be commissioned to design the packaging which will include both the actual container and the graphics that will appear on it.

Right product, right price, right place, right time

A mix is made of a range of ingredients that are blended together. This is very important because, however well designed a product is, or how clever the idea, that on its own will not guarantee success.

When marketing their products, firms need to create a successful mix of:

- the right product
- sold at the right price
- in the right place
- using the most suitable promotion.

These four key ingredients of the 'marketing mix' are often referred to as the 4Ps – Product, Price, Place and Promotion.

A range of advertisements

The target market influences the design of the product – products for children look very different from products for adults

A perfect mix

To create the right marketing mix, businesses have to meet the following conditions:

- The product has to have the right features – for example it must look good and work well.

- The price must be right. Consumers will need to buy the produce in large numbers to produce a healthy profit.

- The goods must be in the right place at the right time. Making sure that goods arrive when and where they are wanted is an important operation.

- The target group needs to be made aware of the existence and availability of the product through promotion. Successful promotion helps a firm to spread its costs over a larger output.

The elements of success

'Dramatize relevant differences. Dramatize a market property. Create a difference.'

The essential aim of any marketing or advertising campaign is to convince consumers that without purchasing a particular product or

brand, they are missing out on something (see pages 42–45). The role of the designer, working with marketing and advertising consultancies, is to develop a product image and psychology which reaches the public.

However, as you will soon realise as you investigate marketing, the message is often concealed. Designs are created not only for their appearance and function but also for their value as status symbols Think of the design of many clothes products, car adverts and cigarette adverts and you will realise that there is more to marketing than just telling people that you have a product to sell.

Many products are created for their value as status

Activity

1 Explain why it is important to determine the term 'target market' for any product.

Key points

- The three functions of marketing are to sell, communicate and persuade.

- Successful marketing depends on the marketing mix of the right product at the right price in the right place at the right time – the 4Ps.

Analysing the product

Uncovering the message

By carrying out a product **analysis** activity on advertisements or promotional leaflets, it is possible to uncover the original intentions of the **designer**.

Product analysis is like writing a **specification** in reverse. Rather than deciding what a product should be by writing a specification, you are looking at the product and trying to work out what the original specification was.

A range of advertisements. What are they saying about the product? Is it clear, or is the message hidden?

Activities

For this activity, you will need a collection of advertisements which could be either paper based or on video. The aim of the activity is to analyse advertising and probe the reasons for their design and appeal.

1 Working in a small group, look carefully at your examples of advertisements. Each person should take turns to explain to the group the following:

a why they selected their example

b what makes the advertisement work

c design details that are important

d who the advertisement is aimed at.

2 Working on your own, analyse at least one of the following:

a advertisements from newspapers and magazines

b examples of shop/store advertising and promotions

c samples of wrappings, packaging.

Use the analysis checklist opposite to produce an A3 presentation illustrating your findings in an interesting and imaginative way for display.

Analysis checklist

In order to use this checklist, simply answer each question as it relates to your own particular example of advertising.

- What is the market for the product or service – who buys it/uses it? What are the visual clues that lead you to this conclusion?

- How is the information conveyed to the buyer – overt (open and obvious who the product is intended for), or covert (hidden or deliberately disguised)?

- What convinces people to buy this product/ service rather than similar brands or alternatives? (Consider the design, the words, the messages.)

- What symbols are associated with the product/service? Are they traditional or modern? (For example, health food products often have pictures of farmyard scenes with horse-drawn ploughs – what do these suggest about the product?)

- Take each advert in turn and consider its design and the processes/systems involved in creating it (lettering, photography, computer graphics, film). How have these been achieved? How effective is the result?

- How important is the design to the marketing of the product? Does the advert provoke? Is it catchy? How does it grab attention?

- Consider the layout and the application of **aesthetics** (whether the advert is pleasing to the eye). How are the following elements used: colour, proportion, balance and symmetry?

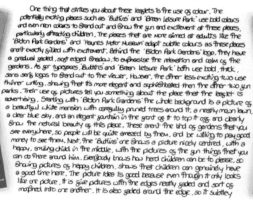

A student's product analysis

Activity

1 Explain how colour can help to create a particular mood or feeling in an advertisement.

Key points

- By carrying out a product analysis activity on a range of advertising materials, it is often possible to work out the original design specification and intentions of the designers.

- Many advertisements have closed messages that are used to provoke and make people really think about the product; other advertisements are completely open and clear.

- Product analysis is a very important part of the **research** for a design project.

- Product analysis is an example of primary research because it is carried out directly on the source material.

Creating identity

The *Oxford English Dictionary* describes identity as:

'the state of having unique identifying characteristics held by no other person or thing – the individual characteristics by which a person or thing is recognized'.

As individuals we are easy to recognize because, generally speaking, we look different. People remember us because of the way we look, speak and behave. Having an identity is just as important for businesses as it is for people.

Using graphics to create identity

Most organizations use visual symbols or **logos** to separate them from other companies and allow the public to recognize them. The best symbols are simple yet very distinctive. They often say something about the organization and give an impression of the quality of the goods or services they offer.

The Q8 oil company is a good example of how companies create visual identity. The company is owned by Kuwait, hence the clever use of simplified initials to indicate its origin. The symbol it uses is simple and uses bold **primary colours**. It is easy to recognize.

The Q8 symbol

The basis of identity

Most graphic identities are based around the use of logos. Logos are everywhere. They are part of a graphic language that we have come to understand and accept.

Logogram, logotype, image, or symbol?

The word logo tends to be used to represent any combination of symbols and type (words), but in fact there are distinct and different elements, or parts in a logo:

- Logogram – this is a design which just uses the initial letters of a company.

- Logotype – the most common form of logo which uses a specially designed typeface to create a distinctive image for an organization.

- Images – these are often used as backgrounds with logograms to communicate to customers the nature of the organization.

- Symbol – this is usually a stylised (simplified) image related to the organization that helps to communicate the product or service.

Combining the elements

A good example of how different elements of a logo are used can be seen by looking at the graphic identity of the company SfE.

A logogram

The company uses the logogram on all of its products. However, this alone does not give a clear visual connection to its main role, which is working with teachers. To improve this, the company combines the logogram with images of schoolchildren which makes a clear visual link with the company's main business. This product handbook show how the combined elements work.

The SfE ringbinder combines a logogram with images of children

The advantage of having a clearly recognizable logo that is used with different elements is that the combination can be changed and customers still recognize the product.

Use of colour

Logos often need to be photocopied and used in black and white as well as colour. Because of this it is important that they are designed with contrasting colours. Contrasting colours make them bold and stand out. A very successful combination is red and yellow. Red is an aggressive colour which stands out and yellow is a submissive colour that drops into the distance.

The colours in this logo work together to produce a well-known image

Trademarks

Trademarks are registered images that can contain a graphic image, company name or slogan. Some companies just use their name on their products as their trademark. Cadbury's, Nestlé and Coca Cola are examples of this. Their trademarks are instantly recognizable even though they do not always use graphic symbols or images.

Trademarks such as this are instantly recognizable

Activity

1 List three features of a successful logo

Key points

- Logo is a general name which describes a graphic identity used to represent an organization.

- Logos can be created from one or a number of different elements.

Corporate identity

What is corporate identity?

The term **corporate identity** relates to the visual images used throughout an organization to create a particular image that it wants to project to its customers.

Not just a logo

Corporate identity is far more than simply a **logo**. It is the way people look, the way they behave, their uniform and the image of all the products and services the organization provides. All of these factors project a particular image that has been carefully **designed**.

A corporate identity

The purpose of corporate identity

Corporate identity is a business strategy designed to produce a consistent and recognizable product. It helps employees to feel that they belong and it provides homogeneity. Homogeneity (uniformity) is the word used to describe a consistent and common approach.

Making a difference

One of the aims of the corporate identity business is to try to help people first to discover whether there is a genuine difference between their business and somebody else's; secondly, to express that difference if it exists; and thirdly, to help them create such a difference, where no real difference exists.

This is particularly important for an organization such as a bank or building society. Because essentially all banks provide a virtually identical service, it is the corporate identity that highlights the uniqueness of each organization.

The service provided by each of the banks is very similar; it is through the corporate identity that any differences are displayed

Types of corporate identity

There are three different approaches to corporate identity, each of which has its advantages:

- **monolithic identity**
- **endorsed identity**
- **branded identity**.

BMW endorses the different models with the name badges

Monolithic identity

A monolithic identity is a singe all-encompassing identity that gives a very similar and constant visual image to all products or services provided by an organization. With a monolithic identity, the same colours are used and the same logo is consistently applied. This is a popular approach for many companies because it ties all their products together.

A good example of a company that has adopted a monolithic identity is MacDonald's. Wherever you go, MacDonald's restaurants look the same. Their corporate identity is clear and bold and contributes to popular appeal.

Endorsed identity

An endorsed identity is often practised by organizations such as car companies. It involves linking different products together with an endorsement, such as a company badge, trademark, or symbol.

A good example of how endorsed identity works is to think about a car company such as BMW. Although each model is different, designed for a different **target market** with different needs, every car incorporates a number of visual clues that link them strongly to the parent company.

BMW is pleased with the quality of its product and therefore is happy to endorse each of the different models. It achieves this through the use of the common name badge and use of similar styling on items such as the radiator grill.

Branded identity

A branded identity is adopted by many confectionery and sweet manufacturers. Although belonging to the parent company, brands have their own identity too. Branded identity allows a company to capitalize on a market and helps to eliminate competitors.

Branded identity is very important because many popular brands have developed what is know as 'brand loyalty' among consumers. To change a brand by linking it to the parent company may risk losing this loyalty.

Branded identity means that companies can capitalize on brand loyalty

Activity

1 Give two reasons why corporate identity design is important to businesses.

Key point

● Corporate identity is far more interesting than simply designing a logo. It is the way that a company creates a particular image for itself across all its products and services.

Posters and merchandising

Selling with graphics

Posters are widely used to generate interest in a product or event. As with all materials that are designed to promote, they must attract people's attention and create interest and desire.

Posters always form the basis of **advertising** campaigns because they are cheap to produce and can be easily displayed in shop windows and on billboards. Posters always contain a mixture of graphics and information.

Posters

Posters usually use photographs or images to attract attention. When an event such as a film or video is being advertised, characters from the film are usually shown. This helps people immediately to recognise and understand what the poster is about.

An exciting part from the play or film is usually shown. Sometimes the photograph is taken directly from the film and at other times it has been **designed** by the graphic designer. When promoting a product such as a film, the name of the film, actors and performers, along with important information such as times and dates, are all included to help make the image effective.

Merchandising

When a new product such as a television programme or film becomes popular, manufacturers often use this success to increase the sales of their own products. This is known as merchandising. Merchandising is good for both companies because it gives free publicity to the film or programme and helps to increase sales of the product.

A range of merchandising

Merchandising is part of product promotion. Promoting a product involves developing ways of making it more popular and increasing sales. Large companies invest huge sums of money in sponsorship, for example. Football teams have company names on their shirts, and players are paid for wearing a particular type of boot.

Most pop bands promote their new CDs or singles by a music tour. One way in which merchandising is used to help promote their tour is by selling T-shirts. People who go to the events want a souvenir and in turn this helps to provide free advertising for the band.

The football club is paid a sum of money to advertise the sponsor's product; in turn the sponsor receives 'free' advertising

Activities

1 Look carefully at the film poster and answer the following questions:

 a How does the poster create impact?

 b What does it tell you about the film?

 c What are the main colours used for the text and why?

2 Give two benefits to the manufacturer of merchandising.

Key points

- Posters are widely used to promote products or services. They use colours, images and slogans to attract, create interest and desire.

- Merchandising means producing products related to a film, television or book. The products use the success of the film to sell themselves.

What type are you?

Type and typography

The word 'type' is another word for a letter or character. You will have all heard of the machine called a typewriter which is similar to a computer keyboard and stamps letters onto paper. The art of letter style and **design** is called **typography**.

Typography is not just about neat lettering or writing. Different letter styles, or typefaces as they are known, can be used to give effect, create meaning or to make an impact. When designing graphic products you need to select typefaces very carefully in order to achieve the outcome you are aiming for.

Size

Typefaces are usually measured by the point system. One point (pt) is approximately 0.35mm. Therefore a 10pt typeface will be 3.5mm high. The size of the type face is important. Usually text that is printed in books is no smaller than 10pt because it is difficult to read. For headings, a much bigger typeface such as 16pt is used. For banner headlines, typefaces as large as 160pts are often used.

Shop fronts are a good source of typographic designs

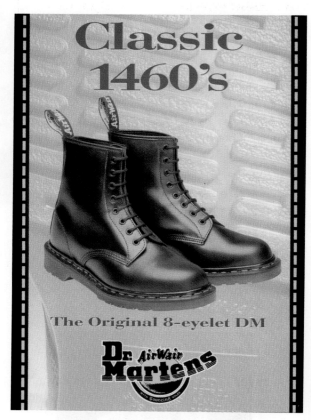

Note the heading of the Doc Martins Classic 1460's poster

To ensure that a typeface is easy to read, designers also have to consider its width and how light or bold it is. A light typeface needs to be larger in order to be easily read, **but it is easier to read a bold or wide typeface**.

Style

There are thousands of different typefaces or fonts to choose from when you design a graphic product, but the main styles are serif, sans serif, freehand and stylized.

Serif typefaces have tails on edges of the letters. Serif typefaces are used for the main text (body text) in books because they are easy on the eye and 'comfortable' to read.

Serif typeface

The word 'sans' comes from the French word which means 'without'. Sans serif typefaces do not have tails; they are plain and clear. Sans serif typefaces are used for information and warning signs because they are clear and simple.

Sans serif typeface

Freehand typefaces are used because they appear to be more personal. They are called freehand because they are often similar in style to a persons own handwriting.

Freehand typeface

Stylized typefaces are designed so that they help to communicate meaning. Stylised typefaces are often found on products such as chocolate bars.

Stylized typeface

Text layout

Text can be arranged in different ways on a page to produce different types of layout. The most common types are:

- centre justified
- right justified
- fully justified

The word justified, or 'justification' as it is sometimes used, means alignment. So, left justified means that the text is aligned to the left, and so on.

Centre Justification

This is when each line of the text needs to be centred on the page or column. It is often used on fold-out leaflets and posters, but is rarely used in books

Left justification

This means that the text is aligned to the left. It is used to line up the text to a margin on the edge of a page or sometimes next to an illustration in the middle of a page.

Right justification

This is the opposite to left justification. It aligns the text to the right side. It is often used to align text next to a picture or photograph.

Fully justified

This is when the text is aligned on both the right and left hand margins. It is often used for columns in newspapers and magazines. Because words vary in length, the spaces between the letters have to be adjusted. Adjusting the spaces between the words is called **kerning**. Kerning is often carried out automatically by word processors.

Activity

1. Design a stylized typeface for a new chocolate bar that is to be called 'Cruncher' Think about how the typeface design will communicate to the customer what the product is like. With careful use of colour, design a letter style that reflects the contents and also gives the impression of a crunch.

Key points

- The size and style of typeface is very important. When designing graphic products, you need to select typefaces very carefully to achieve the desired outcome.

- Typefaces are usually measured using the point (pt) system. Note that 1 pt equals about 3.5mm. For posters and displays, a very large point size is required.

Layout grids

Grids

When graphic **designers** produce layouts for products such as packaging and posters, their designs are usually based upon a **grid**. If you take a close look at this book, you will notice that each page has certain similarities. It uses the same size and style of typeface for headings, sub-headings and body text. The colours are consistent. The position of the page numbers are the same.

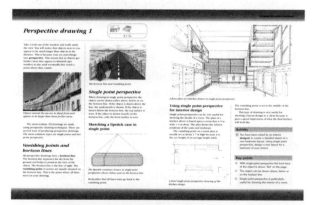

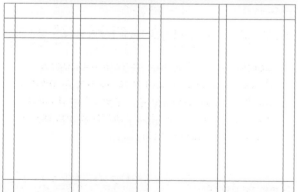

A two-page spread from this book and a tracing of the grid used

You may also notice that all the text is fitted into two columns. This is because the book is based upon a grid. Designers spend a long time thinking about layout and producing ideas and **sketches**.

All newspapers, leaflets and magazines use a grid for their layout. This helps to give the product a visual style, which can be used on every page.

Grids as underlays

As we have already discovered, graphic designers usually base their layout designs on grids. Grids are particularly useful when used as **underlays**. An underlay slips underneath the page you are working on and allows you to trace through. The easiest type of underlay is a line guide. The line guide helps the designer to keep all written text horizontal without having to draw guidelines in pencil on the page.

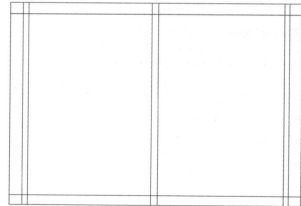

Using a grid such as a line guide makes it easier to present your work consistently neat and accurate

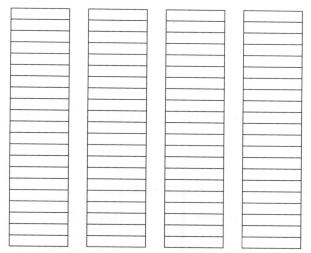
Column guides

Column guides

Column guides are very similar to line guides accept that they separate the page into two, three or four columns.

Column guides are particularly useful when presenting **research** or product **analysis** sheets. They enable you to cut and stick onto the page and keep the writing in a column.

Drawing with grids

When you need to produce accurate sketches quickly, there are a number of different grids that you can use.

Squared grid

Squared grids are most useful for producing **orthographic** sketches. With a squared grid, the front view, end view and plan are easy to place by following the lines on the grid (see page 60).

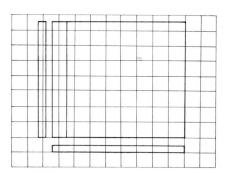
Squared grid

Isometric Grid

Isometric grids consist of lines at 300 from the horizontal, together with vertical lines. Isometric grids are very difficult to make yourself, but you can buy them. Drawing isometric sketches with a grid is very simple and quick (see page 52).

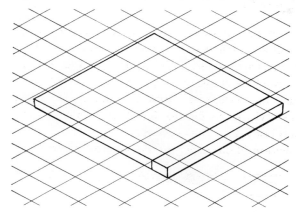
Isometric grid

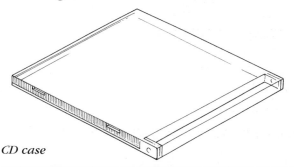
CD case

Activity

1 Collect a number of different magazines. Place a large piece of tracing paper over a double page and using a pencil and ruler, carefully sketch out the grid that has been used to lay out this page.

Key points

● Using grids and underlays helps you to produce work consistently and accurately and saves time.

● Grids help the designer to achieve 'visual continuity' in their designs because they allow for the layout, headings and general arrangement to be consistent.

Ergonomics and anthropometrics

Offices are carefully designed so that people can work efficiently

Ergonomics explained

Whenever you design anything that is going to be used by humans, you must consider **ergonomics**. Ergonomics is the study of how people work, rest and play in their environment, which could be an office, school, factory or even at home. In simple terms ergonomics is about how to make people more efficient at what they do.

A good example of how a product is ergonomically **designed** is a mobile phone. The phone has rounded edges to make it comfortable, the distance between the microphone and the speaker fits the distance between the average adult's ear and mouth and the buttons are well spaced and easy to use. Notice also that the buttons use a bold typeface that is easy to read.

The efficient environment

So, ergonomics is about making things the right shape, size and weight for humans. But what if the room that you are working in is too hot or too cold?

People work best at a room temperature of about 20°C. You cannot work efficiently if you are too hot or too cold. Ergonomics also considers noise, vibration, light, and smell. In fact, if your senses are uncomfortable, you will not work efficiently.

The best offices are ergonically designed. Work desks have been ergonomically designed. Heating, lighting and noise are carefully controlled in offices, so that people are comfortable and work at their best.

Ergonomic graphics

Look at the sign below which is written in an Old English style.

This style of very decorative writing is poorly designed from an ergonomic point of view. It is difficult to read and takes time to work out what it is saying. When designing signs and posters it is important that people can quickly and easily 'get the message'.

116

Size is important

Look at the writing below. Which ones are difficult to read?

Can you read this?

Can you read this?

Can you read this?

Can you read this?

Can you read this?

Can you read this?

The size of the text is very important. If the writing is too small, people will have to strain their eyes to read it.

Style and colour

Some typefaces are easier to read than others. It is important that the one you choose can be easily read. This is particularly important for emergency signs where clarity is very important. Look at the two signs below. Which style would you choose?

DO NOT ENTER

DO NOT ENTER

The way colour is used can greatly affect how efficient a graphic product is. Good ergonomic design requires colour contrasts such as red and white.

Nice and clear   Not so clear

Anthropometrics

Anthropometrics is always used with ergonomics. 'Anthro' means humans and 'metrics' is measurement. Anthropometrics is therefore about human measurements.

Anthropometric data sheets contain information about the range of human dimensions and sizes for all ages.

If you measured the nose length of 10,000 18-year-old men, you would find that the graph produced follows a bell-shaped curve.

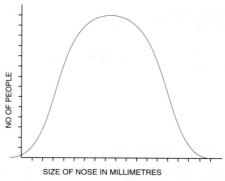

Survey of nose lengths of 10,000 18-year-old men

At the left-hand end of the graph are people with small noses. At the right-hand end are people with large noses. The percentages help us to work out how many of the 10,000 men have small, large or average length noses. The vast majority of men are close to the average. Usually, when we design things we try to consider 90% of the population.

Anthropometric data is produced in a series of tables that can be found in most libraries.

Activities

1 Watch someone preparing a meal at home. See if the kitchen is well designed. Would the meal be prepared quicker if the cooker was moved closer to the sink? Does anything need to be moved to help the cook cut down on time?

2 Explain, giving three examples, how a designer has taken ergonomics into account in the design of a pencil.

Key points

- Ergonomics is the study of how people work, rest and play in their environment – ergonomics is about making people more efficient at what they do.

- Ergonomics is linked to the use of anthropometric data. Anthropometric data provides statistics of human measurements and is used by designers to decide on the most appropriate sizes for their products.

Questions

1 The picture below shows a chocolate bar wrapper.

The logo on this chocolate bar wrapper is part of the company's corporate identity.

a List *four* important features of a successful logo.

b Using *two* examples, explain what is meant by the term corporate identity.

c Give *two* reasons why companies adopt a corporate identity design.

The use of colour is important when establishing a brand identity for a product. Colour is often used to symbolise the purpose of a graphic product.

d Explain what colour you might use to produce an eco-range of washing liquid and why.

2 Design a new logo for a holiday park. The holiday park's name is Eden Way. Your design should:

● use symbols or images that represent a holiday theme

● include the title of the holiday camp in the logo.

3 The picture below shows a poster advertising a holiday resort.

a From the list below, name the type of layout labelled A, B and C.

   box rule   centred   fully justified
   right justified   heading   left justified

b The title has been produced using a 144 pt sans serif typeface. Explain what the terms 144 pt and sans serif typeface mean.

THE FINAL PRINT

The final print 1

A variety of graphic products

The final stage in the production of graphic products takes place at the printer. It is here that the **designs** are produced in the form that they will appear in the shops.

Printing has been used for hundreds of years to produce graphic products. Understanding how graphic products are produced commercially is very important to young designers. When graphic products are designed many decisions need to be made about how they should be printed. The choice of method chosen is determined by such factors as the cost, the quantity required and the quality.

There are five main types of printing:

- **relief printing**
- **intaglio printing**
- **planographic printing**
- **screen printing**
- **dry printing** (photocopying).

Relief printing

It is likely that you will have used a potato to print shapes on to paper when you were young – this is a simple form of relief printing. In relief printing, paper is pressed against a raised surface (relief) in wood, lino or metal. The two most common forms of relief printing are block printing and **letterpress**.

Block printing

Today block printing is mainly used commercially to produce high quality hand-produced prints on graphic products such as wallpaper. Woodblock printing is said to have originated in China in the fourth century AD and was used primarily for Buddhist texts. By the late sixteenth century, block printing was also used for illustrations.

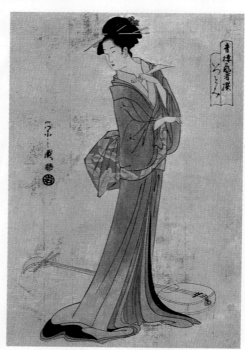

Chinese Buddhist missionairies introduced woodblock printing to Japan where 'ukiyo-e', or pictures of the floating world, became the mainstay of Japanese printmaking for hundreds of years.

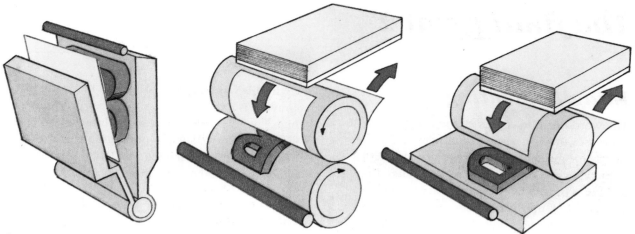

Letterpress printing from a relief image

Letterpress

Letterpress is printing from a relief (raised) image. This can be individual pieces of type (letters) arranged in sentences and held together in a frame, or relief blocks such as wood cuts and photo-engraved metal plates.

The most simple form of letterpress printer is the old-fashioned typewriter. The typewriter presses an inked surface against the paper with force. In this way the raised image prints on to the paper.

Letterpress was once a very common process for producing two-colour prints, but it is now rarely used. It is a costly process to set up because of the time taken to set the metal type and the cost of producing relief plates. Nowadays it is used to print high quality stationery and certain specialist books.

The typewriter is a good example of a letterpress machine

Flexography

Flexography is a very similar relief process to letterpress. It uses flexible rubber or plastic plates for the cylinders of rotary presses. The process is often used for long runs of low cost printing such as packaging, **point of sale** display material and cartons.

Activities

1 What are the five main types of printing?
2 Why is letterpress rarely used today?
3 Give two advantages and two disadvantages to the consumer of the process of block printing.
4 Carry out a product **analysis** of a typewriter. Look carefully at the way it **functions** to help you understand the process of letterpress printing.

Key points

● An understanding of how graphic products are commercially produced is very important to designers.
● Letterpress is no longer thought of as a commercial process.

The final print 2

Intaglio printing

The word **intaglio** covers all the printing processes that are based around etching. Etching simply means engraving the design on to a plate of metal, wood or sometimes glass. When the etching is finished, ink is wiped across the surface filling up the cut lines. Finally, the plate is wiped clean leaving only the ink that remains in the cut lines. The paper is held against the plate and the ink transfers from the engraving on to it.

Gravure

The most widely used commercial application of the intaglio process is **gravure**.

The plates used are reproduced photographically with the images broken into dots (through a screen). These dots are etched on to the plate as cells. The darker parts of the picture have deeper cells than the light areas.

In this way, different **tones** can be produced. Gravure is a widely used process for producing high quality printed products at high volume (in large quantities), such as photographs and glossy magazines. It is most economic on long runs, typically 500 000 to 1 million.

Advantages	Disadvantages
Can be used for the highest quality reproductions	The initial cost of producing the plates is very high, therefore it is only economical on very long runs
Can use lower grade, lighter paper than lithography (see opposite page)	Colour correction is difficult

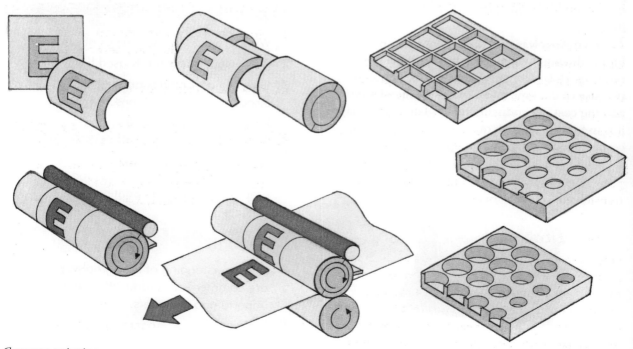

Gravure printing

A lithography printing machine

Planographic printing

Planographic (flat plate) printing is widely used in commercial printing. The most common form of planographic printing is **offset litho**.

Lithography

Lithography is based upon the principle that water and grease do not mix. With lithography the plate is produced photographically and divided into areas that attract grease (ink) and areas that attract water. Before printing the plate is made wet. In this way all the non-printing areas will repel the 'greasy' ink. The paper is pressed on to the plate and the inked image is transferred on to the paper.

Offset litho

Offset litho is the modern method of lithographic printing. The inked image is transferred or offset to the rubber surface (blanket) of a rotating metal cylinder and only then brought into contact with the paper. This brings less water into contact with the paper and enables a finer copy to be produced.

Lithography has become the most widely used print medium and is used for newspaper and magazine production, labels, stationery, packaging and posters. The most sophisticated litho machines will print four process colours (full colour) on both sides of the paper in one pass through the press, and some also fold and gloss the paper.

Lithography printing machines vary in size and complexity. The most common forms are sheet-fed and web-fed lithography:

- Sheet-fed offset litho prints on to single sheets of paper from A4 to double A0 size. Small machines use disposable paper printing plates and are used for 'instant printing' letterheads and business cards in one or two colours up to about 5000 copies. Larger machines are used for medium run (5000–20 000 copies) general colour printing.

- Web-fed offset machines print on to a continuous roll (web). It is much quicker than sheet-fed offset and paper is cheaper on rolls than sheets. However, the set-up time for the machine is longer and therefore web-fed litho is only economical on long print runs.

Activities

1 What are the factors that you would consider when choosing between gravure and lithography?

2 How are darker tones achieved in gravure?

Key point

- Before choosing a printing process, you must decide how many copies are required and what quality will be needed.

The final print 3

Screen printing

Screen printing is probably the most versatile of all printing methods because it allows you to print on to any material with a flat surface, including wood, metal, plastic, fabric and glass. It is relatively simple but is quite a time consuming and labour intensive process, hence it is most economical on short runs.

Screen printing is unlike all other ways of printing and uses a stencil, through which ink is pushed. It is called screen printing because the ink is forced through a fine mesh (called a screen) which helps to spread the ink evenly across the stencil.

Screen printed products

The screen printing process

Screen printing units consist of a vacuum bed (for holding down the paper) and a hinged frame that allows the screen to be raised and lowered. Screen printing can be done completely by hand. It is therefore very cheap for a small number of prints. Automatic screen presses can print up to 6000 copies per hour.

Stencils can be produced by hand or photographically and are not suitable for fine detail or very small type (letter) sizes.

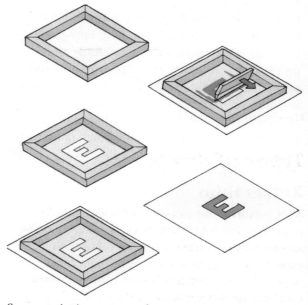

Screen printing process drawings

Dry printing

Dry printing is a very quick, easy and economical way of producing monochrome (black and white) copies. It is based upon the principle of magnetism. On a magnet, there are positive and negative poles. Opposite poles (north and south) attract each other, like poles (north and north, south and south) repel.

In dry printing, the ink has a negative electrical charge which makes it attractive to the positively charged printing area. The ink (often called toner) is held in position electrically until it is fixed by heat.

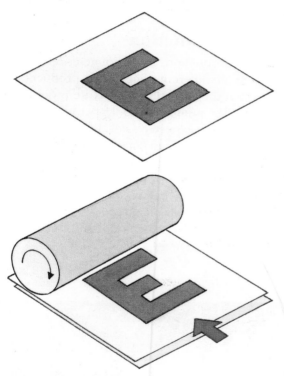

The dry printing process

Types of dry printing

Xerography

Xerography is the general name given to the process used by photocopiers. With xerography, an electrically charged plate is dusted with a negatively charged toner powder. The toner is repelled by the negatively charged image areas on the plate but attracted to the positively charged printing areas.

A photocopier

Laser printers

Laser printers are very common in schools today. They use the dry printing process and can produce very high quality reproductions.

A laser printer

Activities

1 List three products that have been produced by screen printing.

2 Give one advantage and one disadvantage of screen printing.

3 Draw a **flow chart** of the screen printing process.

Key point

- Xerography is too slow a process to be used commercially for longer production runs.

Industrial production

Types of production

When a graphic product is industrially produced, decisions have to be taken about how it will be made and how many are going to be needed.

Making one sign for a hotel is very different from printing the wrappers for a popular chocolate bar when thousands are needed every day.

Designers need to decide very early on in the design process how many products will be needed. This is usually written into the product specification. There are three main types of production:

- **job production**
- **batch production**
- **flow production**.

Each of these types of production has implications on the cost of the product, and sometimes the design.

Job production

Job (or one-off) production occurs when a firm produces specialized, one-off products for its customers. An architect's model is an example of job production. It is unique, requires specialized skills and takes a long time to produce. Job production allows a product to be tailor-made for the customer.

Batch production

In batch production, groups of items move through the different stages of the production process at the same time. Books are produced this way. The number of books per batch is determined by expected sales. For a textbook, this is usually between 2000 and 10 000.

Each section comprises a number of pages (typically 32) and is printed separately. The entire batch is completed before adjusting the machine to print the next section. For books, batch production is the most efficient and cheapest type of production.

An individual architect's model requires a high level of specialist skill and is very time consuming to produce

Job	Batch	Flow
One-off production	Production in batches or groups	Continuous production
Can produce tailor-made products	Involves a high degree of planning between batches	High volume of production means products are produced more cheaply
Requires highly skilled workers and a range of machines	Requires a range of different machines and skills for different batches	Needs one set of machines to produce standardized product
Very flexible process	Quite flexible – changes easy to make	Very inflexible once the machine has been set up – changes difficult to make
Labour intensive	Quite machinery intensive (expensive to set up)	Few workers but very machinery intensive

A comparison of the three main types of production

Books are examples of graphic products that are batch produced. When a batch of books is printed, each section is printed as a separate sheet

Flow production

In the flow production system, products move continuously from one stage of the process to another. This type of production is most appropriate when a large quantity of products are produced. Flow production can be repetitive (repeated when needed) or continuous.

A wrapper for a popular chocolate bar is an example of a graphic product that would be produced by flow production. Chocolate wrappers are produced by flow production because of the vast numbers that are required. Products such as Kit Kat are sold in their millions around the world every year, so there is a continuous need to produce the wrappers. Flow production tends to be very machinery intensive. This means that the amount of machinery needed is high compared to the number of workers involved. This means that initial set-up costs are very high.

Activities

1 What type of production would be used for the following graphic products:

   a a promotional display

   b a daily newspaper

   c a cereal packet?

2 Give two advantages of job production.

Key point

- The type of production chosen depends upon the type of product and the number required.

Manufacturing systems

Planning for manufacturing is often a very complex process that can involve managing a number of people, processes and machines.

In industry, planning is carried out by production engineers. They will identify all the operations that need to be carried out to successfully make the product and then plan the layout of the production line.

The production plan is a detailed and accurate schedule that lists all the operations in the correct sequence and details all the times, materials and resources that are needed.

Stage	
Stage 1 costs	13/12
Manuscript in	16/02
Photo brief	16/03
Artwork brief	16/03
Manuscript to design	16/03
Stage 2 costs	04/04
1st proofs in	06/04
1st proofs out	18/04
2nd proofs in	01/05
2nd proofs out	04/05
3rd proofs in	11/05
3rd proofs out	16/05
Final files in	23/05
Final files out	25/05
Colour proofs in	30/05
Colour proofs out	31/05
Stage 3 costs	06/06
Film in	07/06
Film out	08/06
Ready at printers	03/07
Ready at warehouse	10/07

An example of a production plan

Cell production

Many products require a number of processes to be carried out before they are complete. Often these individual processes are carried out separately by teams of people who work in a cell, such as people working together on a car assembly line. This is called **cell production**.

Look carefully at the pencil case opposite. Make a list of all the different processes you think were used to make this.

A metal pencil case

In-line assembly

Products that have many components and are mass produced are often produced on a continuous assembly line (like a conveyor belt). Products such as televisions and cars need to be assembled in one place with the workers and parts organised to arrive at exactly the right time. Modern assembly lines are very efficient and quick. It can take as little as three hours to build a car from scratch.

In-line assembly of cars is an effective system of production, taking under 24 hours from start to finish

Just-in-time

One of the problems that faced industry was the high cost of storing all the materials, components and other parts needed for long assembly lines.

Traditionally, companies would store enough materials and components (stock) to last for several days. This is a very expensive form of organisation and one which could not continue in the move to **lean production**.

The Toyota Car Company discovered a better system of stock control and called it **just-in-time**. To reduce the space occupied and money tied up by large quantities of stock, Toyota worked out a card ordering system known as 'Kanban'. The rule was simple – no components would be made or ordered unless the instruction was given by the Kanban.

If an assembly worker fitted ten left-hand car doors, a Kanban would then be sent to the production team. The production team would produce another batch of ten left-hand car doors. In theory, these doors would arrive just before the assembly workers' stock ran out, that is, just in time.

The new plan meant that only one hour's worth of materials and components would be kept in stock. Any delays of more than one hour would cause an immediate halt in production of the whole car plant. At first, just-in-time caused chaos, but very soon the Toyota corporation outsold all its main rivals in the car industry.

Toyota is credited with discovering 'just-in-time' management – an efficient system of stock control

With 'just-in-time' stock control, components and materials arrive just in time for production

Activities

1 Choose a graphic product and carry out an industrial production analysis, answering these questions:

   a What method of production would have been used (job, batch or flow) to create the product and why?

   b Would in-line assembly or cell production be the manufacturing system used for the production of this product? Give reasons.

2 List the advantages and disadvantages of just-in-time management.

Key points

● Manufacturers work out detailed production schedules in order to devise the most efficient system of manufacturing.

● Just-in-time stock control helps to minimize time wasted, and saves money by helping to achieve lean production.

From design to print

Before an illustration or a **design** can be printed, a printing plate must be made. The plate is usually made from an aluminium sheet and contains the negative (back to front) photographic image of the picture that needs to be printed.

Producing the image

Unlike text, all pictures or illustrations are either a line drawing, or a **tone** illustration. A line drawing could be a black and white drawing, graph or chart whereas a tone illustration is like a photograph which is made up of shades rather than definite lines. Each type of illustration needs different treatment.

A line drawing of a camera

A tone drawing of a camera

The photographic image used to make a plate is produced using a process camera. A process camera is a large piece of photographic equipment that can have special lenses and filters

A negative image of a line drawing

attached to it. Producing a negative image of a line drawing using a process camera is a very easy process. On a negative line drawing image, all the black lines of the subject appear as transparent lines and the white background appears black and opaque.

Tone illustrations

Tone illustrations need to be broken up into a series of dots before they can be printed. The dark parts of the picture are made from large dots and the light areas from small dots. From a distance the human eye cannot see the individual dots.

Look at the photograph of the skull. It has clear areas of light and dark tones. When you look at an image that has been printed in a magazine or newspaper like this through a magnifying glass, you can quite easily see the different sized dots.

Clear areas of light and dark tones can be seen

To make this pattern of dots, the original photograph is scanned through a screen. A screen is a piece of film that is covered in thousands of tiny dots. like a fine mesh. It has the effect of creating dots on the negative.

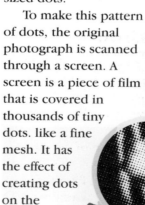

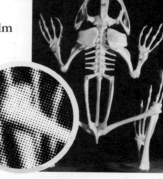

The different sized dots can be seen through a magnifying glass

The density of the screen (the number of dots in a line) affects how sharp the final picture is. The higher the screen size (higher density), the better the quality. Compare the quality of a newspaper picture (screen size 80) with a picture in a magazine which is between 220 and 300.

Colour illustrations

Magazines or books with colour pictures seem to contain a mixture of many colours. At first glance, it appears that thousands of different coloured inks have been used. In fact, all these different colours are produced from just four colours. The four colours are **cyan** (blue), **magenta** (red), yellow and black. These are known in printing technology as the process colours and are referred to as CMYK for short. They represent the three **primary colours** plus black. From these colours, all the other colours can be produced.

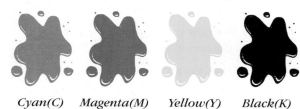

Cyan(C)   Magenta(M)   Yellow(Y)   Black(K)

To produce a full-colour print, the four colours are printed separately one on top of the other. In this way the eye sees all the colours in various amounts and is deceived into thinking that the whole range of colour is present.

Colour separation

To achieve this full-colour effect, four different printing plates of the same image are needed: one to print each colour. When making these plates, the printer uses a process called **colour separation**.

To produce a colour separation of the image, a process camera or **scanner** is used. The process camera uses a special glass filter that only allows one colour through. The camera operator takes four pictures of the same image, but uses a different coloured filter each time.

The most common method of colour separation is to use a special scanner that has built-in colour filters. This method is much less time consuming for the printer. The image is produced through a screen so that each colour is broken up into dots (like for tone illustration described earlier). The scanner produces four separate pieces of film. These in turn are used to make the four printing plates.

The stages of colour separation

Special colour filters are used to make a separate image in each of the four process colours

The four colours are printed on top of each other to produce the final print

Activities

1 Explain how the size of the screen effects the print quality.

2 Draw a block diagram of the stages involved in producing a printing plate for a magazine page.

Key points

● To produce a full-colour print, each of the four process colours – CMYK – have to be separated and printed individually.

● Images can be either line drawings or tone illustrations. Tone and colour illustrations need to be converted into a series of dots by scanning, or photographing them through a screen.

Putting on the gloss

Printing effects

Look closely at this page and then compare it to a computer printout on a plain piece of paper. The pictures in the book look glossy, and the paper doesn't pick up dirty finger prints. This is because the paper used in the book has had a finishing coat of varnish applied to it. In the same way that wood needs to have a coat of varnish to protect it and make it look good, so does paper.

Varnishing

A gloss finish involves applying lacquer or varnish after printing. Varnishing requires an additional stage in the printing process after all the colours have been printed, but before all the cutting and folding takes place. There are four types of varnish in common use:

● Oil-based varnish is a very cheap but it takes a long time to dry, about 4–6 hours.

spot varnish   *matt*

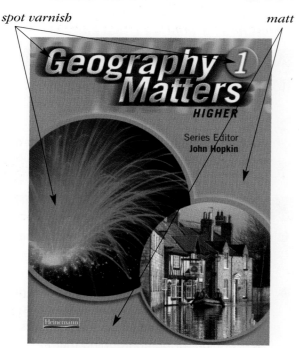

A finishing coat of varnish on a book

● Water-based varnish cannot be applied as part of the normal printing process as it requires a special machine. This adds both time and cost to the process.

● Spirit varnishing, like water-based varnish, requires a special machine. In addition to the extra cost involved with this process, spirit varnishes are now considered to be environmentally unacceptable because of the solvents they contain.

● Ultraviolet (UV) varnish is used to achieve a very high gloss. In this process, the lacquer is applied by a roller and then dried with UV lamps. Most paperback books have this type of varnish.

Special effects

Several special effects can be applied during the printing process. These allow the graphic product to be bent, folded, stamped and cut. The main effects used are:

● **die cutting**
● scoring and perforating
● folding
● **embossing**.

Die cutting

The best way to describe die cutting is to imagine a pastry cutter cutting irregular shapes in pastry – this involves a sharp metal blade pressing down and cutting through the material.

Die cutting is more commonly known as cutting and creasing. It involves the use of special blades attached to the printing machine. Blunt knives are used for creasing (prior to folding) and sharp knives for cutting. With die cutting, many layers of card and paper can be cut in one go. It is especially useful for cutting irregular shapes that cannot be cut on a guillotine.

Scoring and perforating

This is done on board or thicker grades of paper to enable them to be folded. In both **letterpress** and **offset litho**, the scoring rule (like a blade) is joined to the press or cylinder.

Folding

Special formers are fitted to printing machines to allow paper and card to be folded into shape which is particularly useful when making boxes and **point of sale** displays. Usually, the maximum number of layers of thick paper that can be folded is eight.

Folding machine

Embossing

This involves raising the surface of the material with a stamp or press. Embossing is done for effect – to make the surface of the material stand out and be visually more interesting. Embossed products give the impression of being high quality. Embossing is often used on letterheads or certain types of packaging.

Embossed lettering adds to the appeal of the product

Laminating

Laminating involves sandwiching paper or card between two thin layers of clear plastic and then using heat and pressure to fuse them together. The result is a high gloss finish which helps to protect the paper. Lamination is widely used on restaurant menus, for example, because it protects the paper from moisture.

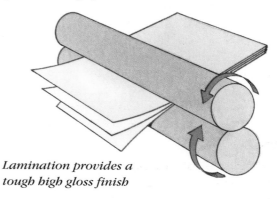

Lamination provides a tough high gloss finish

Activities

1 Give one characteristic of ultraviolet (UV) varnishing.

2 Explain why designers often use embossing as a finishing process.

3 Collect a range of household packaging and carefully take them apart. On each piece of packaging identify:

 a fold lines

 b cut lines

 c any examples of embossing.

Key points

- Varnishing is used as a finishing process on graphic products to provide protection and a high gloss finish.
- Finishing processes add extra cost to the graphic product.
- Many layers of paper and card can be cut automatically using die cutters attached to printing machines. Die cutters can cut intricate shapes.

Questions

Printing processes

The drawing below shows the imprint made by a wooden block used for block printing wallpaper.

1   With the aid of sketches, describe the process of block printing.

2   Give *two* reasons why block printing is used.

3   Block printing is often used to produce hand-made wallpaper. Hand-made wall paper is very expensive.

   a   Give *two* reasons why the cost of this wallpaper is so high.

   b   Describe an alternative printing process that would produce a less expensive wallpaper.

4   A company wishes to produce 10 000 full-colour leaflets to advertise its latest range of cosmetics. The printer has suggested three possible printing processes – gravure, off-set lithography or screen printing. Suggest which printing process you would advise the company to use. Give three reasons for your answer.

Industrial production

A small chain of restaurants has commissioned a printing company to batch produce full-colour menus and point of sale displays.

1   Explain what is meant by the term 'batch production'.

2   Give *two* detailed reasons why the batch production method might have been chosen.

3   Suggest the most likely printing process for batch producing 5000 menus and justify your choice.

4   List two different products whose packaging will be printed using flow production. Explain your answer.

The company has suggested that the menus should be laminated.

5   Give *one* advantage and *one* disadvantage of laminating the menus.

6   Suggest an alternative finish that could be applied to the menus to protect them. Give one reason for your choice.

7   Explain what is meant by the following terms:

   a   just-in-time

   b   lean publication

   c   cell production.

8   A manufacturing specification for a point of sale display says that it should be made from 200 gsm duplex card with a UV spirit lacquer finish. Explain what is meant by the terms:

   a   200 gsm

   b   duplex card

   c   UV spirit lacquer finish.

USING ICT

Using ICT

ICT in D&T

ICT stands for information and communication technology. It relates to how technology can help to make us better informed and to work more efficiently. ICT is not just about the Internet, it is about a whole range of different ways of communicating. Using ICT could help you improve the quality and accuracy of your graphic product coursework. ICT could help to improve the quality of your work in **design** and technology in a number of ways. What follows are a few suggestions.

Research

Surf the Internet to find out information about your project. Access pages on the **World Wide Web** directly. Use e-mail to ask companies for information about their products. Visit virtual factories on the Internet to see how manufacturing is carried out in industry.

Design ideas

Use a **digital camera** and photo editing software to change existing pictures. Use computer-aided design software to create ideas quickly and easily. These can be rotated and modified in numerous different ways.

Development

Use computer-aided manufacturing software to make a model of your solution. Use a **database** or CD-ROM to find out more about the most appropriate materials for your design. One student produced this simple model using a computer-controlled vinyl cutter.

Images from a digital camera can be used as a background for designs

Final design

Use a full 3D **scanner** and cutter to manufacture your design from your high quality **prototype** model. Use graphic or publishing software to produce publicity materials to **advertise** your product.

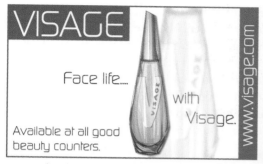

Example of an advert for your product

Planning

Use a spreadsheet to work out detailed costings of your product. Use a **template** for the production schedule designed using lay out software, or using **flow chart** design software to generate a flow chart.

Making

Computer-aided manufacture can be used to make the final product, such as a computer-controlled **plotter/cutter**.

Point of sale display produced with the aid of a computer-controlled plotter/cutter

Video camera linked to a computer

Evaluation

Hold a video conference about your product. E-mail digital pictures taken using a digital camera to companies and individuals for them to **analyse** (ask their permission first!). Show your ideas to a client or a person in industry by using a video camera that is linked to a computer. Use a word processing package to write a detailed report about your product and use a scanner to illustrate any changes made.

Activity

1 List three stages in the design process and for each explain how ICT may support the work of the designer.

Key points

● Careful use of ICT will improve the quality of all your design and making activities.

● Using ICT is an essential requirement for success at GCSE.

Scanners and digital cameras

Scanners

In recent years, graphic **designers** have come to rely increasingly on **scanners** in the design of graphic products.

Flatbed scanners are usually A3 or A4 size so they are ideal for design work. A scanner is a device that creates an electronic map of a picture. This map is a made up of a series of dots or **pixels**. The quality of the picture is determined by how many dots there are per square millimetre. This is known as the resolution. The higher the resolution, the better the quality of the picture.

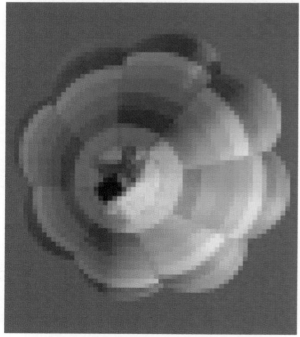

A scanner produces an electronic map of the image made up of a series of dots or pixels

High resolution scanned, colour images take up a lot of computer memory and they are often too large to store on a floppy disk. Always try to save your files using a compressed file format such as .jpg.

Using scanners

Scanners are particularly useful in design and technology projects because they allow you to add photographs and realistic pictures to your work. This will help you to make high quality graphic products that look like the real thing. Also, scanners operate as a colour photocopier so you can make copies of graphic work and include it in your design folders.

A student's CD cover design using scanned images

Digital cameras

Digital cameras are a cross between a normal camera and a scanner. You use them like a normal camera but instead of the images being captured on photographic film, they are saved on a computer disk.

Digital cameras have a small screen at the back of the camera that allows you to see the picture once you have taken it. This means that if you are not happy with the result, you can delete it and start again.

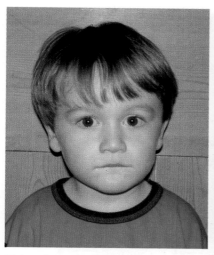  

Using digital editing software, photos such as that on the left can easily be manipulated. Adding effects to an image can add interest. In Photoshop, 'chrome' was selected from the filter menu for the effect in the centre picture. The 'ocean ripple' filter was selected for the effect on the right

Transferring the pictures to the computer

Once the pictures have been taken, they need to be transferred to a computer. Most digital cameras are connected to the computer with a cable, and special software is used to transfer the images. This process is called **uploading** (the opposite of downloading). Once the images have been uploaded to the computer, they are saved as files that can be opened and closed in the normal way. This allows you to use them either directly as they are or load them into design software and modify them to suit.

Digital editing

When pictures have been scanned or uploaded to the computer they are saved as digital images. These images can now be changed or edited using photo editing software. The most common forms of editing are cropping (cutting an image down to size), rotating and resizing. In addition, the individual pixels can have their colour changed, be deleted or deformed in some way. Doing this will help you to create interesting graphic products.

Changing and creating interest

Often pictures have minor errors on them such as 'red eyes' on people caused by flash photography. This can easily be altered using digital editing software.

Once an image has been uploaded, many different effects (called filters) can be applied to it. Adding effects such as twirls, distortions and perspective can form the basis of creative graphic product design.

Activity

1 Give two reasons why scanners are so popular with designers.

Key points

- Scanners and digital cameras provide designers with the images for graphic product design.
- Digital editing allows images to be changed and distorted to create interesting designs.

Digital cameras in design

Producing underlays using a digital camera

Digital cameras are a useful tool because they will enable you to produce **underlays** which help to improve the quality of your drawing and **sketching**.

As part of **design** and technology project work, you are often required to carry out product **analysis**. The presentation of this activity always requires a picture of the object. However, some objects such as a camera are very difficult products to draw well. In such cases, a drawing **template** will help you to produce a quality image.

Producing a drawing template

The first stage in producing a drawing template is to take an image of the object using a digital camera. Then **upload** the image into the digital editing software. The image can now be cut away from the background. This is important so that clear outlines of the object can be traced by the computer.

The camera has been cut away from the background

The final stage in producing the template is to use the 'find the edges' facility on the digital editing software. This produces an outline tracing of the camera which you can then use for your own drawing.

An outline tracing of the camera

Print out the outline and place it under your design sheet. Trace the picture. It is a good idea to use a lightbox, so that the underlay shows through more clearly.

Alternatively, digital editing software can be used for placing a coloured background behind the image. This technique is useful for producing a presentation drawing of your final design.

A different background is placed behind the camera

Digital editing software

Commerical quality graphic products can be produced using digital editing software. Images taken by a digital camera or downloaded form the Internet can be manipulated and combined with other images to create useful graphic products.

A design project

'Use photo editing software to produce a credit card.'

This design project was given to a group of students on a graphic products course. The original pictures were downloaded from the Internet. Alternatively, they could have been **scanned** from a book or uploaded from a digital camera.

The first task was to create a credit card template. The front and back of an existing credit card were scanned and using editing software, the name and details of the user were changed. By using the existing template, the final images look very realistic. A range of images can then be chosen – these could be from a film or images of people or places. The final task is to merge the chosen images with the credit card.

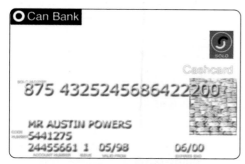

Scanned images of the front and back of a credit card

The students chose an image of Austin Powers

The original image of the credit card is merged with another image

Once printed, the front and back images of the credit card can be joined together with double-sided tape to produce a very realistic graphic product.

Activity

1 Explain two ways in which the digital camera can be used in the design of graphic products.

Key points

- The digital camera is a very effective tool for producing underlays that will help to improve the quality of drawing and sketching.
- High quality graphic products can be easily and quickly produced using digital editing.
- High quality graphic products can be easily and quickly produced using digital editing.

Cyber graphics

World at your fingertips

A whole new language has developed over the past few years since the dawn of the Internet. Words like **cyberspace**, e-mail and **search engine** are now part of our everyday vocabulary. The Internet (sometimes called the information superhighway) is a network of interconnected computers around the world. This new world where people are linked together electronically is called cyberspace.

Using the Internet

All you need to plug into cyberspace is a computer, a modem and a telephone line. A modem is an electronic device that converts the digital signals from the computer into sound signals that can then be sent down the telephone line. A modem works in reverse when it receives signals from other people. Because it is relatively easy for anyone to publish material on the Internet, there is an astonishing range of information that can be found. This can be invaluable to you when you need to carry out **research** for your **design** and technology projects.

Looking at web sites

In the same way that people are able to find out where we live by using our postal address, each company or individual who sets up an information page on the Internet has an address. Searching for a particular address will lead you to a **web site**.

Finding a web site

The Cabaret Mechanical Theatre is an interesting site full of mechanical moving toys. The web site address for the theatre is: http://wwwcabaret.com. Have a look at the site here.

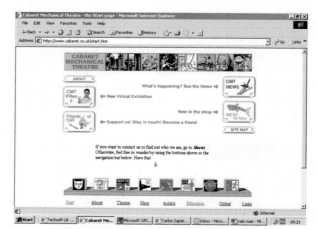

The Cabaret Mechanical Theatre web site

The web site is full of information about the theatre and many other attractions. It is divided up into sections to enable you to find your way around (navigate) more easily. The site allows people to find out about mechanical sculptures and also to buy products online, from the comfort of their own chair.

The design of web sites like this must be clear and simple. Just like a book, web sites must have a contents list, clear headings and simple instructions. They must also be interesting and informative. The very best web sites make you feel as though you are virtually there!

Designing a web page

In the same way that graphic designers have traditionally designed leaflets, brochures and **advertising** campaigns, they are now frequently called upon to design web pages. Web page design is different to designing a book or leaflet. Pages do not have to fit into a particular **grid** or size, they can be as long or short as necessary and there is no limit on the number of pictures or images used.

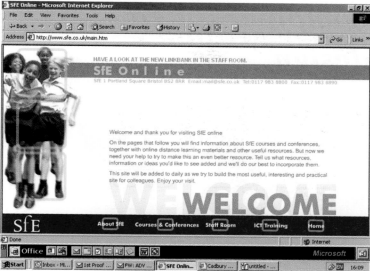

Design in action

One such new designer is Owen Jackson, a computer specialist who manages the web site for the educational training company SfE. Owen is a professional web site designer. The SfE web site has 4000 pages of useful content for schools and teachers. When designing a web site, many factors have to be taken into account.

Making it instantly recognisable

To make the web page instantly recognizable, Owen knew that he had to include the company's **logo** plus a connection with education. The use of the children and the logo helps people to recognize the site.

Clear layout

When designing a website, it is important to remember that everyone will see the site slightly differently. This is because the quality of computer monitors can vary enormously. Therefore, unlike a book which is the same for all readers, small, complex images and text may not work.

Reading text on a computer screen can be quite difficult. The choice of text, its size and colour are very important to the design. Owen decided to design the web site using a conventional layout with simple yet bold images and good colour contrast.

The SfE web site combines information about forthcoming events with online conference facilities (http:/www.sfe.co.uk). The image of children on the SfE web site helps to make the site instantly recognizable

Unlike a text book which is written and then occasionally changed, a web page must be constantly updated.

Activity

1 What is meant by the following terms:

  a e-mail

  b World Wide Web

  c modem?

Key point

- The Internet provides a vast source of information which you can use for your design and technology project. However, no credit will be given by examiners to students who merely download pages of information and do nothing with it.

- Make sure that any information from the Internet is carefully selected and **analysed** before being included within your design folder.

Computer-aided design

A student using a CAD program

The computer is just a tool

Many people think that somehow computers will replace **designers**. This is not the case. However, they can make the work of a designer much quicker and easier. As the name suggests, computer-aided design (**CAD**) is a computer software program that assists designers in their work.

Features of CAD programs

Most computer-aided design software requires you to produce **orthographic** (2D) drawings (see page 60). From these 2D drawings CAD programs will generate 3D views. However, some programs will produce fully detailed working drawings for you. These programs have a library of all the correct symbols, and will automatically add the dimensions to your work as you draw. As with any other drawing package, CAD software lets you fill areas with colour or with **hatched** lines.

Speeding things up and getting it right

When we draw things by hand, whenever we make a mistake, we have to rub it out and start again. Sometimes we need to change something half way through a drawing. All these things are time consuming and frustrating to the designer. With CAD, making changes such as resizing is very easy to do. Being able to rotate or duplicate an object is a very useful feature.

CAD in action

Computers are widely used to model components and products on the screen which means that designs can be **evaluated** before they are made.

Computer-aided design is widely used in industry. Using CAD, designers can see a model of an object. This means that a product can be seen from all angles, simply by rotating the image. A car designer for example can open and close doors on a car, change colours and wheel types all at the click of a mouse.

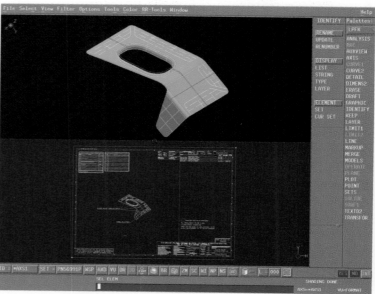

Computer-aided design of a car body part

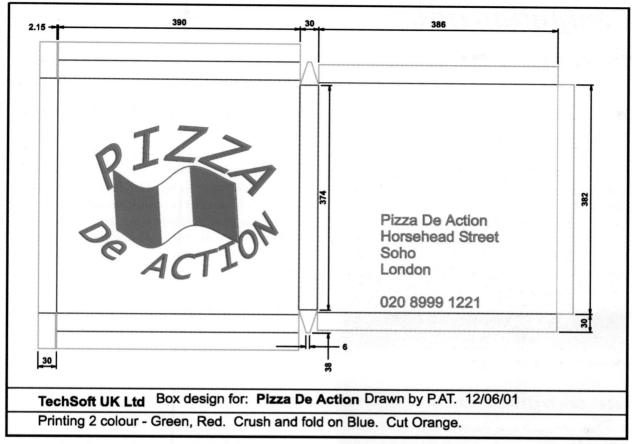

| 2.15 | 390 | 30 | 386 |

374

382

30

6

38

30

Pizza De Action
Horsehead Street
Soho
London

020 8999 1221

| **TechSoft UK Ltd** | Box design for: **Pizza De Action** | Drawn by P.AT. | 12/06/01 |

Printing 2 colour - Green, Red. Crush and fold on Blue. Cut Orange.

Working drawings save time and help you produce drawings that are accurate

Working drawings

In your design and technology projects, the most useful way of using CAD is to help you produce working drawings. A working drawing gives dimensions and all the details needed to make your designs.

Activities

1 List three objects that you think have been designed with the use of CAD.

2 Explain the advantages and disadvantages to the designer of using CAD when designing.

Key points

● Computer-aided design (CAD) software is not a replacement for the designer – it does not come up with ideas.

● Computer-aided design is a very useful tool for the designer. It provides the means for modelling ideas.

● Computer modelling means that ideas can be tested for appearance, size and **functional** details without having to actually make anything.

● CAD saves time and helps to ensure accuracy and precision.

Computer-aided manufacture

5.1.3h, 5.1.4e, 5.1.8b, 5.1.8c, 5.1.8j

In control

Computers help **designers** to design products and have the advantage of being quicker and more accurate than humans. The same is true for making products. Computers are fitted into machines to control their movements. The computer is given a set of instructions in the form of a computer program that tells it exactly what to do. Unlike humans, computers do not need a break – they don't go on holiday and they can work 24 hours a day, seven days a week.

The use of CAM in production

In industry, more and more manufacturing processes are controlled by computers. Robots can do dangerous tasks which would be unsafe for humans. With the help of computer-aided manufacturing (**CAM**) production is now very fast. Today large motor manufacturers such as Volkswagen can produce a complete car in less than 24 hours.

Today, about 85% of a new car is made by computer-controlled machinery

CAM and graphic products

Computer-aided manufacture is widely used for the manufacture of graphic products. The starting point for this process is the final design or the working drawing. The device that is going to make the product is connected to the computer by a cable and is set up with the correct materials. The CAM machine is able to understand the commands from the computer and follows these instructions.

Making signs

Very thin plastic (vinyl) can be accurately cut out and used to make signs by a CAM cutter. A CAM cutter works by following the coordinates of a line drawing produced on a computer with a knife. As the drawing is 'plotted out', the knife accurately cuts the outline of the shape. When finished, the self adhesive vinyl is peeled off from the backing and can then be applied to signs or other objects. CAM cutters work from co-ordinates, so they cannot be used for cutting a **scanned** image or digital photo. This is because scanned images are produced as a series of dots (see page 138).

A CAM cutter

The sign is first designed using a **CAD** program. The size of the sign must be accurately worked out before cutting.

When the sign has been cut, the waste is 'picked out' and the vinyl is transferred to the plastic base using special adhesive film.

Some CAM machines use a rotating cutter rather than a static knife. These are called router or milling machines. Large CAM milling machines are widely used in industry, but they are very expensive. Small CAM machines can be very useful within graphic products as engraving tools. Designs can be cut out of solid plastic and used as plaques or **logos** on bigger products.

An example of a student's work using CAM. The logo is machined on to clear acrylic that has been painted black

Scanner/cutters

Many CAM machines used in school do not need to be linked to computers. They have a scanner which can make an exact copy of a product.

The picture shows a scanner/cutter. The design is fed into the machine and a copy is cut directly on to the vinyl.

A scanner/cutter

On the right is a 3D scanner/cutter. A full body scan of the object is made and a model is then cut out. The model can be bigger or smaller. This is particularly useful for making components for models that have to be very accurate.

A 3D scanner/cutter

Embroidery

Graphic product design often involves designing logos for companies and organisations. One way that these logos are used is on uniforms. Computer-controlled sewing machines can be used to embroider the logo on to the uniform.

These sewing machines work from scanned images of designs. The machine is set up with the right colour cotton and the design is produced.

Computer-controlled embroidery is useful for transferring logos on to clothes

Activity

1 List three advantages to the manufacturer of using computer-aided manufacturing.

Key points

- Computer-aided making (CAM) enables manufacturers to produce high quality products quickly and accurately.

- In modern manufacturing such as motor car production as much as 85% of the work is carried out by computer controlled machinery.

Questions

1 A company that makes a range of graphic products is considering investing in computer-aided manufacturing equipment.

   a A partially completed spider diagram of the points that need to be considered before making such an investment is shown below. Complete the spider diagram by adding further points that should be considered.

   b Select *two* important points from your spider diagram. Give a detailed explanation of each.

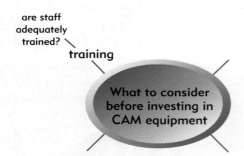

2 The picture below shows a point of sale display.

Explain *two* ways that computer-aided design may have helped the designer of this point of sale display.

3 Explain what is meant by the term computer modelling.

4 Explain *two* advantages of computer-aided manufacturing.

5 Explain why an image from a scanner cannot be linked directly to a computer-controlled cutter.

6 Explain what the following expressions mean:

   a uploading

   b digital imaging

   c World Wide Web

   d resolution

   e pixel.

7 For each of the following stages in the design process, explain, giving one different example for each, how ICT can be used to help the designer:

   a research

   b design ideas

   c development

   d planning

   e making

   f evaluation.

8 The following abbreviations are commonly used in ICT. Say what each abbreviation means:

   a DTP

   b .bmp

   c .jpeg

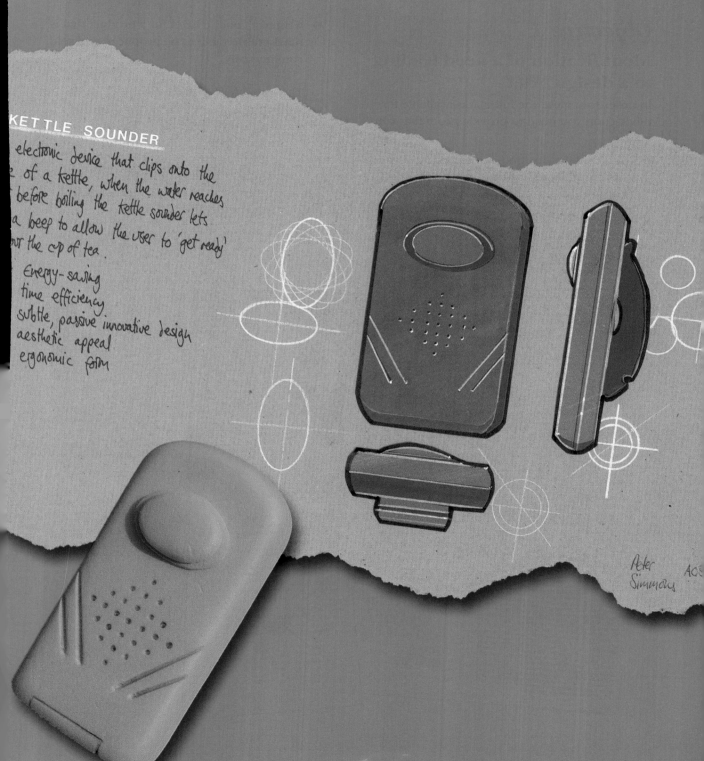

KETTLE SOUNDER

electronic device that clips onto the
of a kettle, when the water reaches
before boiling the kettle sounder lets
a beep to allow the user to 'get ready'
the cup of tea.

Energy-saving
time efficiency
subtle, passive innovative design
aesthetic appeal
ergonomic form

Peter
Simmons

Internal assessment

Objective 1

Identification of a need leading to a design brief

In order to achieve the full marks available for this section you need to provide proof that you have:

- described the **design** need using a variety of communication methods (words and graphics)
- clearly said who the range of users for the intended product may be

- written a concise **brief** for a product that is **marketable** (able to be produced and sold commercially).

The examples below show how this evidence could be produced. A mind map or **spider diagram** shows that the candidate has considered a variety of design needs and possible project ideas.

The exploration shows that a range of users has been considered and the brief is justified from a range of possible alternatives.

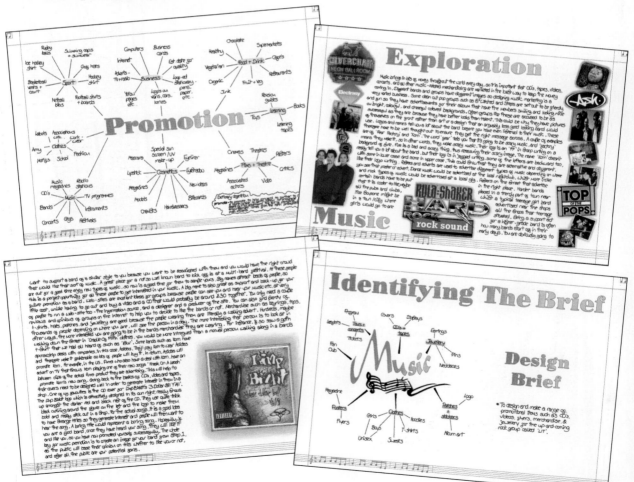

Objective 2

Research into the design brief that leads to a specification

In order to achieve the full marks available for this section you need to provide proof that you have:

- examined the purpose, form and **function** of the product

- carried out **research** such as **surveys** and product **analysis** into how products fulfil the needs of the users; the results must be **evaluated**

- collected and recorded data relevant to the intended product and its users

- developed a detailed **specification** which *must* include details about **batch production** capability.

The examples below show how this evidence could be produced. A specific **questionnaire** is produced with the results analysed and evaluated. A product analysis of existing products is carried out and a detailed specification produced. Alternative means of research could include letters to companies, using the Internet, CD-ROMs, or other secondary sources such as books and catalogues. The most important thing to remember is that you *must* only include relevant material that has been analysed and evaluated.

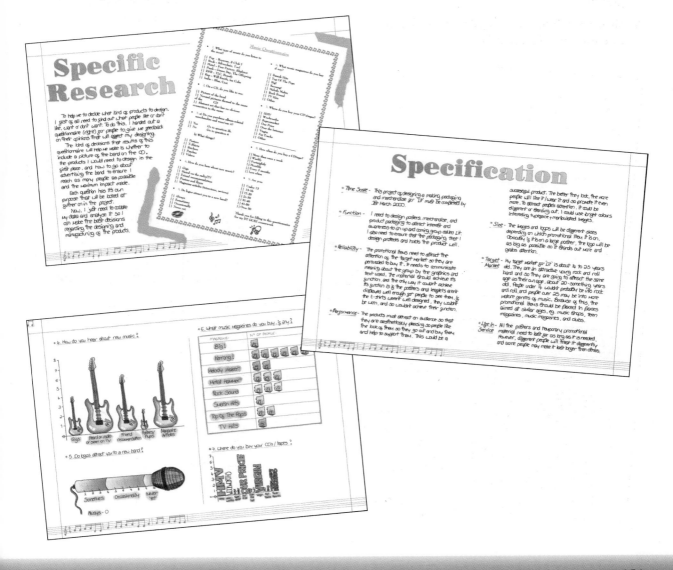

Objective 3

Generating design ideas

In order to achieve the full marks available for this section you need to provide proof that you have:

- produced a *range* of different but appropriate ideas (a range is more than three)

- annotated your ideas relating them to the **specification** by detailed **evaluation**

- identified a suitable **design** idea that has the potential to be developed further

- used ICT in your designing

- used a wide range of graphic techniques which are produced to a very high standard.

The examples below show how this evidence could be produced. A range of ideas for a **logo** are produced. Different typefaces and designs are considered. The ideas are annotated with evaluative comment relating to the specification. The chosen idea is modified and improved using computer-aided design, with an improved solution printed out and pasted on to the design sheet.

Objective 4

Product development

In order to achieve the full marks available for this section you need to provide proof that that you have:

- carried out investigation and testing into a chosen idea that has led you to make decisions about materials, production methods and the appropriate use of standard components

- made further modifications or improvements in order to produce the optimum design

- modelled the idea to ensure that it meets the specification requirements (modelling can be either physical using paper and card or modelling using computer-aided design software)

- developed a system of **quality control** to ensure accuracy during making

- developed a final product or manufacturing specification that gives details of the product.

The examples below show how this evidence could be produced. The logo which forms part of the **corporate identity** is modelled and tested on a CD insert. Ideas are further tested and modelled using ICT to produce a range of different products. Products such as a **point of sale** display could be physically made and tested for properties such as stability and strength. Finally, a manufacturing specification is produced which outlines details of how quality is to be maintained during volume production.

Objective 5

Product planning and realization

In order to achieve the full marks available for this section you need to provide proof that you have:

- produced a plan of action that considers materials, standard components, equipment processes, and health and safety

- selected and used tools and processes safely

- economically prepared and used materials

- produced a high quality product or range of products.

The examples below show how this evidence could be produced. A production schedule or **flow chart** could be used as long as it shows the appropriate detail. The final product **portfolio** should demonstrate a range of very high quality graphic products that are produced using ICT.

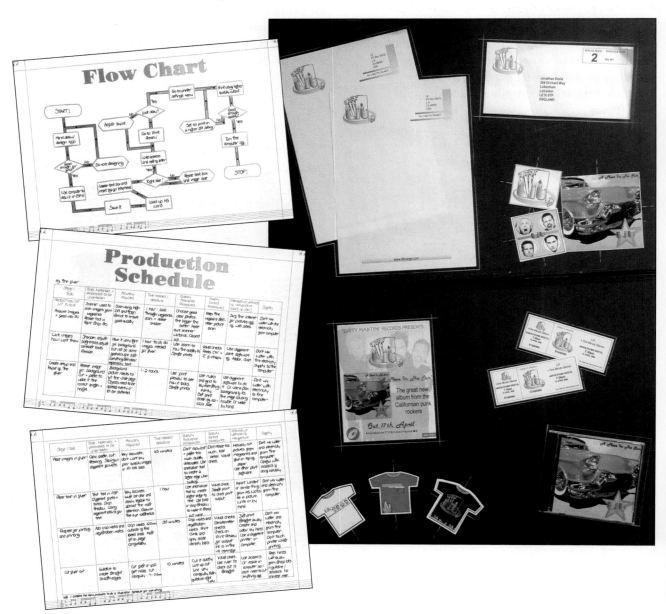

Objective 6

Evaluation and testing

In order to achieve the full marks available for this section you need to provide proof that you have:

- fully **evaluated** the final product(s) against the **design specification** ensuring suitability for the intended users

- carried out testing, drawing reasoned conclusions about necessary improvements or modifications

- considered how effectively you have used your time and the available resources

- **analysed** how effective your **quality control** system has been in the production of the **prototype**.

The examples below show how this evidence could be produced. A highly detailed evaluation that relates fully to the initial design specification is produced. Each heading used for the design specification is considered in turn. The evaluation suggests modifications for future improvements although it lacks **sketches** that would help to communicate those ideas.

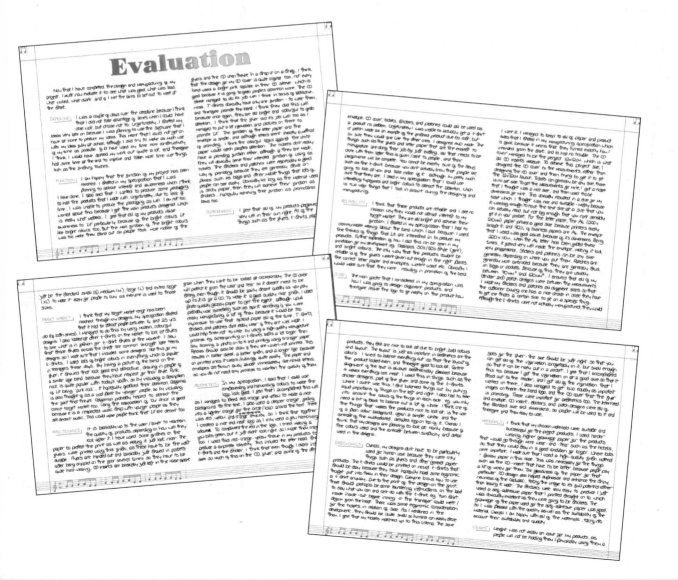

Glossary

acrylic a brittle plastic commonly known as perspex

adhesive a bonding agent used to join two materials

advertising a means of promoting a product

aesthetics how various graphic elements combine to make a thing pleasing to look at

analyse to study closely and ask questions such as who, what, where, when, why and how

anthropometrics the study of measurements of human beings and their movements

axonometric *see* planometric

batch production where a number of items are made at the same time

bisector a line that cuts a line in two

brand identity how a product is recognised

brief a short statement of a problem or need

CAD computer-aided design

CAM computer-aided manufacture

cell production teams of people working together on a production line

closed loop a system with feedback

colour separation a method of separating out the four process colours prior to printing

colour bars printer's marks used as a means of checking colour quality

complementary colours colours opposite each other on a colour wheel which go well together

continuous production when products are made one after the other

corporate identity the 'whole' graphic image of a company

crating boxes used to help 3D sketching

criteria requirements of a product

cyan a form of blue used in colour printing

cyberspace the name given to the Internet

database a collection of information stored on a computer program

design the process of solving problems through the development of ideas to produce a solution

designer person who produces design ideas for client's needs

die cutting industrial cutting process

digital camera a device which takes pictures and stores them directly on a computer disk

development the process of taking an idea and improving/modifying it in order to achieve the best possible solution (*see also* net)

digital editing the process of using software to modify scanned images

elevation another name for 'view' on an orthographic drawing

embossing producing a raised surface on a material

endorsed identity a type of corporate identity

ergonomics how products and places are designed to be efficient for humans to use

evaluation judgements made about ideas and products against the original specification

feint a light weight of marking usually achieved with a hard pencil

flexography printing process which uses rubber or plastic printing plates

flow chart symbols used to present a process graphically

flow production continuous production

foamboard a modelling material

function what a product or process is expected to do

ghost a feint practice line drawn on paper

gsm grams per square metre

gravure a form of four-colour colour printing based upon the intaglio method. Used for high volume production runs

grids devices used by graphic designers to help lay out a page

hatching lines drawn at an angle of 45 degrees
horizon line the line of sight on a perspective drawing
hue the actual colour

incremental dimensioning dimensions that follow on from the last
intaglio printing print processes based upon the principle of etching
isometric a method of drawing objects in three dimensions using 30-degree axes

jig a template used for cutting
job production one off or small scale production
justify to give reasons for choices
just-in-time an industrial method of stock control

kerning spacing between letters

laminating (graphic products) sealing paper between two sheets of thin plastic
lean production when fixed and variable costs of production are kept to a minimum
letterpress a simple form of printing
lithography a form of printing
logotype commonly called logo, a device used to help people associate a product with an organisation

magenta a form of red used in colour printing
marketing the selling of a product or service to a consumer
mass production the production in large numbers of a product
MDF medium density fibreboard
mock-up a model of a design – often full size – to allow evaluation
monolithic identity a type of corporate identity

net the name given to the flat outline of a package – often called a development

oblique a form of 3D drawing
offset litho a variation of the lithography printing process

open loop a system with no feedback
orthographic a form of technical drawing where an object is drawn from different views

perspective the appearance objects give of being smaller the further away they are
pictogram a simple graphic picture without words that conveys information
pixel an individual unit of a digital image
planographic printing print processes that use plates
planometric projection (axinometric) a pictorial drawing method based upon a plan that has been rotated (usually through 45 degrees)
plotter/cutter a computer-aided manufacturing device
point of sale graphic products used to advertise a product used in shops or stores which are often placed 'on the counter'
portfolio (often shortened to 'folio') the presentation of design work
primary colours red, yellow and blue
prototype the initial version of a product used for testing

resolution the density of dots or pixels on an image

quality assurance systems written down to avoid failures in manufacture
quality control tests made on products after they have been made to test their accuracy
qualitative information based upon opinion or observation
quantitative data that can be measured
questionnaire a survey made up of related questions which help to find out people's views

relief printing print processes using 'raised surfaces', e.g. block printing and letterpress
rendering applying colour or texture to a drawing
research the gathering and analysing of information

scale representing dimensions on a drawing in proportion which can be greater or smaller

scanner a device that produces a digital image

screen printing a small scale printing technique using a silk screen

search engine software on the Internet that will search for information

secondary colours purple, green and orange

section an orthographic view showing a cut through view

sketch a freehand drawing

specification the criteria that the final solution must achieve

spider diagram a means of presenting the results of a brainstorm or 'ideas' session

survey research carried out by questioning

system a group of processes organised to perform a task

target market the type of people or age group a product is aimed at

template a shape used for marking out

testing checking the outcome against the specification

thermoplastics a plastic that always returns to its original shape when heated (plastic memory)

tolerance the acceptable amount of error

tone the amount of light or dark

typography the study of letter styles

underlay a paper layout which goes under a designer's page to assist with layout

uploading loading an image from a camera into a computer

vacuum forming a process which forms a thin plastic sheet around a mould – used for blister packing

vanishing point in perspective drawing where construction lines meet

visual continuity linking various graphics on a product using common colours, images and typefaces

web page/site information page on the Internet

World Wide Web another name for the Internet

xerography a dry printing process commonly used by photocopiers

Index